The
Memory
Key

The

Memory
Key

Unlock the
Secrets to
Remembering

Fiona McPherson

BARNES
&NOBLE
BOOKS

NEW YORK

2004 Barnes & Noble Books

ISBN 0-7607-6252-X

Printed and bound in the United States of America

04 05 06 07 08 09 M 9 8 7 6 5 4 3 2 1

Permissions

Grateful acknowledgement is made for permission to reprint material from the following:

Experimental material quoted on page 54 was taken from:
Cantor, J. & Engle, R.W. 1993. Working memory capacity as long-term memory activation: An individual-differences approach. *Journal of Experimental Psychology: Learning, Memory and Cognition, 19,* 1101-1114. © American Psychological Association.

The diagrams appearing on pages 56-57 were taken from:
Broadbent, D.E., Cooper, P.J. & Broadbent, M.H. 1978. A comparison of hierarchical and matrix retrieval schemes in recall. *Journal of Experimental Psychology: Human Learning and Memory, 4,* 486-497. © American Psychological Association.

Experimental material quoted on pages 78-79 was taken from:
Daneman, M. & Carpenter, P.A. 1980. Individual differences in working memory and reading. *Journal of Verbal Learning and Verbal Behavior, 19,* 450-466. © Academic Press.

The two tables on page 121 were taken from:
Robinson, D.H. & Kiewra, K.A. 1995. Visual argument: Graphic organizers are superior to outlines in improving learning from text. *Journal of Educational Psychology, 87,* 455-467. © American Psychological Association.

CONTENTS

CHAPTER 1

HOW TO PERMANENTLY IMPROVE YOUR MEMORY

Courses on how to improve your memory very rarely have any long-lasting effect. It is not enough to learn tricks—to permanently improve your memory you need to understand enough about how memory works to know why and how and when different learning and retrieval strategies are useful.

Most memory-improvement programs do not result in long-lasting change. For 2500 years, "experts" have claimed to be able to improve a person's memory. For most of that time the methods have been the same. But despite the proven effectiveness of these strategies, despite the established validity of the principles, people rarely improve their memory permanently. Even intensive, month-long courses rarely bring about permanent memory improvement.

Why do people who try to improve their memory fail to do so? Not because they are unintelligent or lazy, but because the memory improvement programs are flawed. They are based on effective strategies. They are based on valid principles. But they are flawed because they have put in the "too-hard" basket the information you need to improve your memory. This book aims to fill this gap.

Memory is Plural!

One of the reasons behind the failure of most memory improvement programs to achieve long-lasting improvement is that "memory" is really a category like "sport." Would you say, "I want to improve my sport?" Of course not. But you might say, "I want to improve my tennis" (or golf or swimming).

Memory is not one thing. The feats of memory that so impress us are not evidence of a "photographic" memory or any other innate talent. Being able to memorize a string of 80 digits after seeing them once is a trick anyone can learn—if they wish to devote months of training and practicing to the skill.

But the trick does not generalize to other types of memory. The person who sweats for months to master longer and longer strings of digits will be no better at remembering shopping lists. Chess experts take years to develop their phenomenal memory for the arrangement of chess pieces, but that doesn't make them any better at remembering a speech or what they did last Tuesday.

Surveys have found that there are over 100 memory tasks in everyday life that can cause people problems. Each of these tasks requires a different strategy.

Don't panic! One hundred sounds like a lot, but think for a moment how many different techniques you have for simply getting through the day. Putting on your shoes is a different technique from putting on a shirt; making the toast is an entirely different skill from cleaning your teeth. You probably use 100 different skills before you've gone out the door!

Moreover, you're not starting from scratch. You already have many memory skills, and you're probably quite happy with your level of competence at some of them. What it comes down to is identifying your needs. Don't say "I want to improve my memory," say "I want to improve these specific memory skills."

Identify the memory tasks you want to be more skilled at.

Before you go any further, ask yourself why you want to improve your memory. Why do you think you have a "poor" memory? Here are the memory tasks that most commonly cause problems:

➡ Putting a name to a face.

➡ Putting a face to a name.

➤ Remembering in what context you have seen someone (e.g., "local librarian").

➤ Remembering important dates (birthdays, appointments, anniversaries, etc).

➤ Remembering to do something at a particular time.

➤ Remembering information you have studied.

➤ Remembering the names of things (e.g., computer jargon, business strategies, books, plants, recipes).

➤ Remembering how to do something (e.g., computer procedures, craft techniques, domestic tasks).

➤ Remembering details of someone you have met—names of children and partner, any problems they may have been having last time you talked, etc.

➤ Knowing there's something you need to remember but you can't think what it is.

➤ Remembering whether you've done something.

➤ Remembering where you've put something.

➤ Remembering when/where something happened (e.g., where you bought something; where you read something).

Be specific. Think of particular occasions when you have been embarrassed by your memory failure, or annoyed with yourself over your forgetfulness. Write them down (there's a worksheet on page 11). Use these specific instances as a springboard for working out your needs. If you were mortified the time you forgot your best friend's birthday, write that down. Then consider whether this points to a general memory task you want to be better at (remembering significant dates), or whether you merely want to ensure a better memory for one or two dates of particular importance.

If specific instances of memory failure point to general memory tasks that you wish to be better at, write down the general task. If only the specific instance is of interest to you, write down the specific task.

Here is a sample:

O—⚷

Memory tasks I want to be better at:

⇒ Remembering personal details my friends tell me.

⇒ Remembering interesting things I read.

⇒ Remembering the names of people at my tennis club.

⇒ Remembering my partner's and my nieces' birthdays.

⇒ Remembering things I have to do today.

⇒ Remembering information I have studied

———

If you want to achieve genuine memory improvement, this is a vital, utterly necessary step. So do take the time to think about what you want to achieve before going any further.

Consider the "costs"

Another problem with many memory training programs is that too little attention is paid to the costs of particular learning strategies in terms of the effort and time required.

For example, one of the classic memory strategies is the "method of loci." This strategy requires you to memorize some physical object that has distinct locations (for example, your house, a familiar route, a classroom). You then use this structure as a base for any information you want to remember. So for a shopping list, you might picture bread on the doormat, potatoes hanging from the coat hook, apples in the sink, and so on. This strategy was supposedly invented in 477 B.C., and people have been learning it ever since—but how many people have ever used it more than once or twice? It involves more effort than most of us want to put in.

Strategies such as the method of loci and the pegword system do work, but very few people want to put the effort into making them work. That's not laziness, that's an appreciation of costs versus benefits. The cost of using these strategies is rarely worth the benefits. The amount of effort involved in having an old envelope stuck to the fridge with a magnet and writing down shopping needs as they come up is much less than the mental effort needed for me to produce vivid mental images for each item I need.

Memory task priority list

Memory Task	Effort Rating			Priority Rating
	LOTS	SOME	LITTLE	
Remembering information I have studied				
Remembering someone's name/face				
Remembering important dates				
Remembering to do something				

For a strategy to have value it must be not only effective but also useful. That means the benefit of it to you must be worth the cost to you. Some people find it very easy to create memorable images, and for them the cost of such a strategy is low. Some people may rate a particular memory task as so important to them that they are prepared to invest a great deal of time and effort into improving skills that would help them.

Before you learn a skill, assess whether it is worth the time and effort to you.

Look at your list of the memory tasks you are poor at. Now ask yourself: How important are these tasks to you? You may be poor at remembering people's names, but perhaps you don't really care. You may already be reasonably good at remembering information you have studied, but perhaps it is really important to you to be better.

Beside the tasks on your list, put a rating as to how much effort you're prepared to put into improving your skills for that task. The ratings could be simple comments indicating the amount of effort you are prepared to put in (lots, not much, some, etc.), or could be numbers indicating your priority order. You may find doing both helpful.

Now that you have your targets worked out, let's see what you need to do to achieve them.

What you need to know to improve your memory skills

Learn how memory works

Although I have emphasized that you cannot improve "memory," but instead must target specific memory skills, that doesn't mean that memory skills should be acquired in a vacuum. You can learn to cook without any understanding of basic chemistry, but you'll be far better at adapting recipes and creating new ones if you understand the role of the various ingredients (for example, whether the eggs are included to thicken, to bind, or to leaven).

Research has found that people are most likely to apply appropriate learning and remembering strategies successfully when they have also been taught general information about how the mind works.

The more you understand about how memory works, the more likely you are to benefit from instruction in particular memory skills.

When you have a good general understanding of how memory works, different learning strategies make much more sense. You will remember them more easily, because they are part of your general understanding. You will be able to adapt them to different situations, because you understand why they work and which aspects are important. You will be able to recognize which skills are useful in different situations. Not least important, because you understand why the strategies work, you will have much greater confidence in them.

Understanding how memory works:

⇒ Helps you remember different memory skills.

⇒ Helps you recognize which skill to use.

⇒ Helps you adapt your skills to new situations.

⇒ Gives you confidence in the skills.

⇒ Increases the likelihood that you will use the skills.

Believe in the strategy and your ability to use it

Confidence in a particular technique doesn't come about merely because you have been told it's really useful, nor even by trying it out yourself. To be really convinced of a strategy's usefulness, you need to not only experience for yourself its use in everyday situations, you need to understand *why* it works. You also need to believe in your own ability to use the strategy successfully and appropriately—to do that you need to *master* the skill, not simply "learn" it.

**Mastering a memory skill
means making
it a habit.**

Think of driving a car. In the beginning there were so many different things to think about, but eventually they became routine, automatic. You know you have mastered a skill when you no longer have to think about it.

As it is with driving a car, playing the piano, pruning the roses, a memory skill is mastered when it becomes automatic. And once it becomes automatic you're safe! An automatic, over-learned skill is part of your "permastore." Like the permafrost that never melts, memories in your permastore are never lost.

More importantly, if the skill can be performed automatically, the cost of applying it falls dramatically. The time is less; the effort is much less. Reducing the cost makes using the skill a much more attractive proposition. An over-learned skill is therefore much more likely to be used.

You are more likely to use a skill if:
⇒ You are convinced it helps you remember.
⇒ You understand why it helps you remember
⇒ You know when and when not to use it.
⇒ You are confident that you can use the skill.

Understand your own capabilities

I believe part of the reason for people's lack of confidence in their own skills is the association we commonly make between learning and intelligence. If a person appears to learn facts easily, we assume they are intelligent. A person who has trouble learning is assumed to be less intelligent. Although some people find it easier than others to learn appropriate skills and see when to apply them effectively, being skilled at learning is a learned skill. You can be "smart" and poor at learning; you can be "average" and good at learning. Whether or not you *use* memory-improvement strategies depends more on how much you know about your memory processes than how intelligent you are.

The key to good learning lies not only in your knowledge of how memory works, and your flexible and appropriate use of different strategies, but also in your ability to understand your own capabilities.

You're not likely to use efficient strategies if you don't realize how poorly you have learned something or how unlikely you are to remember it. You're not going to apply a strategy well if you are blithely unaware that you have completely misunderstood the information.

An effective learner:

⇒ Knows how memory works.

⇒ Has many memory skills and can apply them appropriately.

⇒ Monitors and understands their own learning behavior.

Putting it together

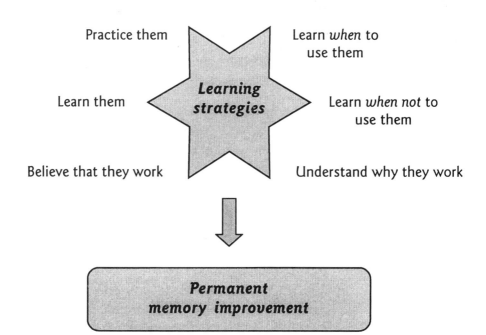

Practice them

Learn *when* to use them

Learn them

Learning strategies

Learn *when not* to use them

Believe that they work

Understand why they work

Permanent memory improvement

Main Ideas

To permanently improve your ability to remember, it is not enough to learn specific memory skills.

To permanently improve your memory, you also need:

- Knowledge about the different sorts of learning tasks, and when different learning strategies are appropriate.

- Knowledge about the process of memory, how it works and why it fails.

- Faith in yourself and your abilities.

Chapter 2

What Comes Out Is What Went In

Memories are not photographs. They are paintings. You *create* your memories. How easily you remember depends on how well you created the memory. The key to remembering is creating memories that will be found easily

The building blocks of memory

To understand how memory works, you need to understand what memory *is*. Clues to the hidden workings of the mind can be seen in the mistakes we make.

The other day I had to take the cat to the vet. While I was out I planned to return a library book and mail some letters. I put the letters and the book on the seat next to me. The cat went in the back.

The cat wailed piteously. In a hurry to get home, distracted by the cat, I stopped beside the mailbox and grabbed the letters. Just about to release them into the hole, I froze. I was about to mail my library book. (Well, it was quite a thin one.)

Now certainly part of the reason for this mistake was that I was in a hurry and distracted. If your mind is not on the job, if you're operating on "automatic pilot," this sort of mistake is common. But saying I wasn't paying attention doesn't really explain why this sort of mistake happened.

These mistakes happen because your actions are based on what's in your head, not directly on the world. In my head, there wasn't a library book, nor a pile of letters. Instead my mind had created two *internal representations*, with properties of their own—not necessarily, and certainly not entirely, the properties that the things themselves had.

I knew when I was creating the representation that it didn't need to be remembered for very long. I also knew that there were only two attributes that were of interest: where it was, and what I was going to do with it.

And there you have the nub of the problem. Two representations in my mind: one reads "sitting on front passenger seat" and "mail it;" the other reads "sitting on front passenger seat" and "return it to library." Given that I wasn't paying any attention to the particular things that were sitting on the front passenger seat, I had a 50-percent chance of getting it right.

Remembering is not simply about finding automatically stored replicas of things that you have experienced. Memories are *codes*, and the type of code, or internal representation that a memory has does not depend on the memory itself, but on how you coded it. Any memory can be coded in a number of different ways. The particular code you create for it will determine how easily you will find it later.

It also determines *what* you find. In the outside world the object might be a library book called *The Psychology of Anomalous Experience* by Graham Reed, in an orange and gray soft-cover, about one-half inch thick, approximately 5" x 8" in size, about 25 years old. But my memory code is based on what I consider important and relevant in the particular circumstances. In this case, my memory code may not have included any permanent attributes of the object, merely two entirely temporary ones—present location and my intention with it.

What you find in memory,
what you remember,
is a matter of the memory code
you created in the first place.

How memory works

Information is infinite

It's a common myth that everything you have ever experienced is recorded in loving and exact detail in the neurons of your brain. If it were true, where would the line be drawn?

Look around the room—have you recorded for posterity every mark on the floor, every dustball? Look away, then back again—have you made another recording?

Imagine everything experienced being stored helter skelter, with no understanding needed, no picking and choosing of what is important. Every time a baby wakes, the scene, the sights, the sounds, the smells, the feeling of cloth against skin, the feeling of moving muscles and of bowel motions, all of it would be faithfully recorded. Every detail would be repeated again and again as it was experienced anew—every minute, every second, every millisecond.

Without selection, without the focus of attention picking and choosing what's worth keeping and what's not, there is an infinity of information to be stored. Indeed, who says the baby has to be awake? Even asleep, sounds, smells, feelings in the skin and muscles can be perceived.

The first, most fundamental principle is that memory codes are created from selected information.

We are not blank slates waiting to be written on, receiving every detail with humble gratitude. We are *users* of information, and the first thing we do with information is choose what to keep.

Is your memory a junk-heap or a storage system?

If we remembered every single thing, then quite possibly memory would be a junk heap—an attic into which everything is thrown willy-nilly "for a rainy day." And, like searching that attic, searching such a memory would be a time-consuming, frustrating business. Unless of course we had recently stored it away and it was by the door.

But memory is a structure. It has been constructed, and is being re-constructed. Laws constrain and guide the building process. If your memory seems like an attic full of junk, it's because you don't understand the design principles.

Association is the foundation stone of thought

To a large extent the principles of memory are the principles of thought.

We associate things in our minds. You say "bread" and I say "butter;" you say "cat" and I say "dog." So familiar is this characteristic of our mental processes we tend to take it for granted. But this ability is telling us something important about how we think and remember.

The associations we make reflect the way our memory codes are organized.

Memory is held in a pattern, not in a place

On paper we may draw a number of dots, like so:

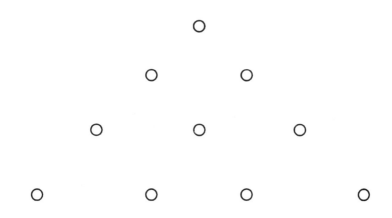

and we see a pyramid. But in the world outside the mind, the pyramid doesn't exist. It exists on paper only because we mentally "fill in" the lines connecting the dots. Without these lines, the dots are not a pyramid. They are not any sort of structure. They are simply a scattering of dots.

"Memory" is the name we give to our collection of memory codes. But, unlike our pyramid of dots, memory *is* a structure, because the dots (codes) really are connected. It is the links between memory codes that form the structure of memory.

For example, consider the concept "cat." There is quite a lot of information in my head about cats. In the picture below I have selected just a few bits of information to give the flavor of memory codes and how they are linked.

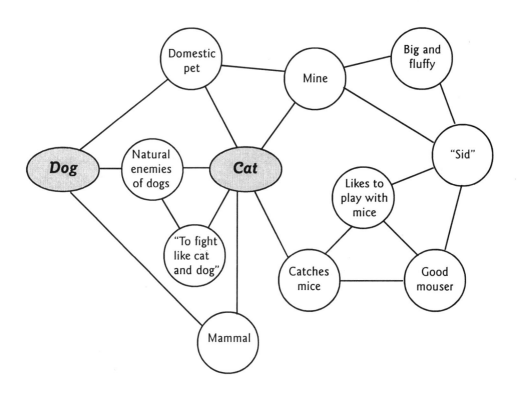

A memory code is a microcosm of memory. What we call memory is a *network* of linked memory codes. But a memory code is itself made up of a number of *bits*, each of which encodes one piece of information. For example, the memory code for "cat" includes such bits as "catches mice" and "domestic pet." A memory code is therefore also a network.

How the network operates

Clearly the boundaries between memory codes are fuzzy: see how my memory code for my own cat merges in with my memory code for the more abstract "cat" concept; the memory code for dog shares some bits with the memory code for cat. Drawing a circle around a bunch of memory bits and labeling it a particular code is to some extent an arbitrary action.

When a particular memory bit is *activated*, the activation spreads along the links that bit has. The bits that belong to the same memory code will usually be very strongly linked to each other, therefore when one part of a memory code is activated, the whole code is activated. Other memory codes will be directly linked to that memory code too (as "dog" is to "cat" in the example). Depending on the strength of those links, they too will be activated.

This is a fundamental principle of memory, of thought—the *domino principle*: if one memory code is activated, many other codes will also become active.

It's not necessary for links to be physically close. When we talk of links being "close" or "distant" we are speaking metaphorically. Even the bits of a code need not be physically close to each other.

Basic principles of how memory works:

⇒ The **code principle**: memories are selected and manipulated, to *represent* experiences not *reproduce* them.

⇒ The **network principle**: memory consists of links between associated codes.

⇒ The **domino principle**: the activation of one code triggers connected codes.

Encoding and retrieving

"Remembering" can be separated into two main processes:

•◦ putting information in

•◦ getting information out

Putting information in involves changing the information into a memory code, hence the term *encoding. Getting the information out* is known as *retrieving.*

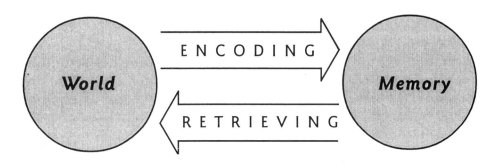

Encoding and retrieving are two halves of the same coin, two sides of the same door. How we think the information will be retrieved will affect how it is encoded. (That was evident in my experience with the letters and the library book.) Furthermore, the way in which information is encoded affects how easily the information can be retrieved.

**The key to remembering is to create codes
that are easily found.**

For example, we've all had the experience of not being able to name a familiar face seen in the "wrong" place. Maybe it's the attendant at your local service station. However often you see him, if you never see him anywhere but at the service station you will almost certainly find it difficult to remember who he is if one day you see him in the "wrong" place. And the more the place is different from the usual context, the harder it will be to retrieve the needed information. So if you see him at the shops near the service station, it might only take you a moment to make the connection; but if you see him in a completely unexpected place—say, when you are on holiday in a distant town—it may take you hours or even days (perhaps not until you see him again in his accustomed place).

23

This occurs because the information about the particular person (*local service station attendant*) is encoded under a particular location (*local service station*). *Local service station* will trigger *local service station attendant* fastest; *local* will probably soon trigger *local service station*, and similarly *service station* will soon trigger *local service station*. But if you can't find a code that will eventually lead to *local service station*, then you won't remember whose familiar face you saw.

On the other hand, if the attendant also belonged to your tennis club, your memory code for the actual person will be more individual. Not just *local service station attendant*, but "Tom who works at the service station and belongs to my tennis club." Your memory code here is different, not so dominated by place or function. Therefore you are far more likely to recognize him out of context.

If you want to reliably recognize someone whom you consistently meet in one particular context you need to create a memory code that gives due weight to individual characteristics.

You create and re-create your memory. If you don't find what you're looking for, if you can't 'remember," then the reason lies in how you have constructed the memory code.

To create a memory code that you can find,
you need to know what you will be looking for.

Are selected
bits of
information

Are created
by you

**Memory
codes**

Are linked
together in a
network

Trigger each
other

Putting it together

Main Ideas

☙ Memory is a code, *not* a recording.

☙ Memory codes are linked to each other in a network. Accessing one item activates those items that are closely linked.

☙ The ease with which information is remembered depends on:

1. Which aspects you selected to include in your memory code.

2. Which aspects you gave most emphasis to.

To create a memory code that's easily found, think about what you will be looking for.

Chapter 3

Finding Is Tricky When You Don't Know Where to Look

An effective memory code is one that can be found easily. A large part of what makes a good code lies in the links it has with other codes, because it is through its links that a code is found. How easily a code is found depends largely on the original encoding.

To find a code, follow a trail

Memories are codes that shift and change as new information comes in, as our perspective and opinions change. Memories are not cast in stone, they are written in sand. But we can follow tracks in the sand.

Remembering is about finding a particular memory code in the complex network of codes that is memory. To find a code, we follow a trail.

For example, think of seeing the service station attendant away from the station. If you wanted to retrieve the identity of this annoyingly familiar face, you would try to track it down by asking yourself a number of questions:

- Have I seen this person recently?
  Yes.

- Do I see this person regularly?
  Yes.

- ❧ To do with work?
  No.

- ❧ To do with children?
  No.

- ❧ Lives nearby?
  No.

- ❧ Service person?
  Yes.

- ❧ Librarian?
  No.

- ❧ Supermarket checkout?
  No.

- ❧ Service station?
  Yes!

An effective search follows a good trail.

A good trail needs a good starting point

Retrieval cues trigger memory search

You could of course have gone completely off the rails by answering yes to, say, the question whether the person had some connection with your children. The questions which define our trail, the bits of information that prompt our recall, are called *retrieval* or *recall cues*, and your success at remembering is wholly dependent on how good they are. Retrieval cues signpost the trails.

Successful retrieval hinges on good recall cues.

Imagine that you have been asked to name as many countries as you can. You would probably start with your own country, then move on to your country's closest neighbors. After that, it becomes more problematic. Initially you might keep with the geographical association and simply move around the globe, but because countries are not lined up neatly, at some point you're going to change tack. The strategy you are most likely to come up with is using continental labels as recall cues.

The order in which you go through these reveals which recall cues are strongest—which continents you are most familiar with. But a number of countries are not clearly part of any continental grouping. To recall these you need different cues; for example, "islands—Pacific." Some countries will be part of a continent, but their association with that continent may be very weak. You might think of Iran primarily in terms of its religious leaders, not as a country of Asia. If someone said "pyramid" to you, no doubt Egypt would immediately spring to mind, but it might well be overlooked if you're looking for countries of Africa.

The key to a successful search is finding the right signpost.

Exercise 3.1

Read carefully through the following list of 28 words twice, then shut the book and write down on a piece of paper as many words as you can remember, in any order.

Rose, pineapple, tights, sofa, archery, truck, ape, pomegranate, dress, tennis, gondola, crocus, vanity, gazelle, trousers, banana, bus, table, sailing, fox, daisy, hat, cabinet, scooter, softball, squirrel, mango, hyacinth.

These 28 words belong to seven different categories: flowers, fruit, clothing, furniture, sport, vehicles, and mammals. On another piece of paper, write down these category labels. Now see how many words you can recall under each label. Compare this with the number of words you recalled earlier.

Most people find that the category cues improve their recall.

What makes an effective signpost?

I'm afraid there is no rule that governs this. Although memory trainers tend to focus on the straightforward advice that recall cues should be funny or bizarre or rhyming, the question of whether a recall cue is effective is not quite that simple. Any memory code can be an effective recall cue. The effectiveness of a recall cue is measured by its results.

An effective recall cue leads, fairly easily, to the *target* memory code. The category label "vehicle" is a perfectly adequate cue for "bus" or 'truck," because they are examples of the category that come very readily to mind. "Gondola," on the other hand, is not likely to be readily accessed from "vehicle," although it clearly does belong to the category.

An effective recall cue begins a path to the target that is short and well-traveled.

Effective recall cues are actively generated

Your ability to generate recall cues may be critical to your successful remembering. Sometimes we are handed the perfect recall cue on a plate, but this is a matter of good fortune. Much of the time our target memory code will not be directly linked to our first recall cue. Instead we will be required to follow a trail of linked codes. The first cue will activate codes directly linked to it, and they in turn will activate those codes linked to them. The memory codes that act as triggers or prompts—the codes between the first recall cue and the target code—are known as *secondary recall cues*.

You can of course simply play the association game. This means that you let yourself be a passive spectator while codes trigger others in a way that reflects the structure of memory. However, while this can be entertaining, it is not a particularly effective way to search for a specific memory.

A far more effective way of searching is to *actively* generate recall cues (*generation strategy*). For example, a person trying to recall members of a familiar category, such as foods, will remember more if they can generate category members that might work as additional recall cues. You might start by thinking "fruit," which would act as a secondary recall cue. When you run out of fruit, you might move on to "vegetables," and so on.

You usually have a better memory for items that you have generated yourself compared to items that have been presented to you, probably because they have more meaning for you.

> **Your skill at generating secondary recall cues is critical in deciding whether or not you will find the target information.**

The basic principle underlying an effective generation strategy is that potential targets are generated in a systematic fashion that prevents the person from generating the same concepts again and again.

Exercise 3.2

A. Your insurance company has just called to say that your insurance has lapsed because you haven't paid the bill. Your checkbook assures you that you made out a check three days ago, but you can't remember mailing it. What recall cues might prompt your memory?

B. You see a familiar face at the supermarket, but can't remember where you know the person from. What recall cues might prompt your memory?

C. You see a person you know—you remember that she belongs to your tennis club—but you cannot remember her name. What recall cues might prompt your memory?

(Suggestions can be found at the end of the chapter.)

The importance of context

If the key to a successful search is finding the right signpost, the question becomes, how do we know which is the right signpost?

Which trail you select—which signpost you think is correct—depends a great deal on *context*.

Context guides the direction of your thoughts.

The information that you find interesting or relevant on one occasion is not necessarily the same information that you judge as worth encoding on another occasion. The information that is emphasized on one occasion is not necessarily stressed on another occasion. Context determines how you experience and encode information. Accordingly, context is a major factor in determining how closely linked your memory code for an experience is to a particular retrieval cue.

For example, suppose you went to a concert, and the most important parts of the experience to you were that your friend made you so late you missed the first half-hour, that you ended up standing by the door because the seats were so bad, and that you missed a really great show on TV because of this awful experience. Two years later, when your friend says, "Do you remember that time we were at a concert and we ran into that woman from Telecom during the intermission?", you are not likely to remember this event from the concert visit. Assuming you had been to a number of concerts together, this is not likely to be a great cue. On the other hand, if your friend says, "remember that concert we were so late for—you were sooo grumpy," that is much more likely to do the trick.

Every experience contains a wealth of information from which we choose the bits that will be used as a basis for encoding. Context sets us up to pay more attention to some aspects rather than others. Even mood, our own emotional state, is part of the context. So is the physical environment.

For example, in one rather dramatic experiment, two groups of scuba divers learned a list of 40 words, one group learning the words on a beach and the other group ten feet underwater. When asked to recall the words, those divers who were tested in the place in which they had studied the material did better than those who were tested in the other location.

In most everyday situations we have little control over the major contextual factors surrounding the information we are encoding or trying to find. However, in more formal learning situations, there is a greater potential to control some of these factors.

Using context effects in formal study:

Study the material to be examined at the same time of day that the exam is scheduled for.

⇒ The longer the delay between your studying and the exam, the more separated you should make the gaps between your periods of study. This helps increase the chance that at least one of the study contexts will match the exam context (in terms of the weather, your mood, your state of mind, and so on).

⇒ The longer the test delay, the less study and test contexts are likely to overlap, therefore the more important it is that the two study contexts should vary as much as possible.

⇒ If the time of the test is known, massive study just before the test is better—study and test contexts (at least as regards mood and mental attitude) are more likely to be similar.

⇒ But cramming just before an exam is no good for remembering in the long-term—again, partly because of context. By maximizing the similarity between the learning and the recall contexts, you have improved your chance of remembering the information in that particular context. But if you do this you won't have the experience of encoding the material in a number of different contexts, and you will need this experience to assist your recall in different situations.

What really determines the ease of recall is the degree to which the encoding and retrieval contexts match (the context effect). If encoding occurs in more than one context, the chance is greater that the context when retrieving will be similar. The greater the number of encoding contexts, the greater the chance of the retrieval context being similar.

Context is a two-edged sword. The more the retrieval context is like the context at the time of encoding, the more likely it is that appropriate recall cues will be triggered, because the trail you follow is more likely to be in the correct direction. However, if the retrieval context is unlike the encoding context, it can mislead you as to the right trail to follow.

Faces and context:
An example

Faces are strongly connected to context. When we try to remember who someone is, our first thought is almost invariably, *where* do I know them from? A person whom you only see in one particular place is remembered more easily (but only in that place).

In one study that looked at face recognition in everyday life, one participant believed for a long time that a person she saw in two different places was actually two different people!

Context then is important for two main reasons:

•◆ Context influences the meaning placed on the selected information, and hence how it is encoded.

•◆ Context also may be encoded *with* the selected material, and provide additional retrieval cues.

Context provides potential recall cues.

Context can guide you in the right direction, or point you in the wrong direction.

The less the retrieval context matches the encoding context, the more important is your skill at generating cues.

The goal is the guide

To know if you are going in the right direction you need a guide, because trails can be quite long, and there are so many trails.

While contextual information guides your search, you need something else to help you assess whether the trail you are following is likely to lead you to the target. The information that you use to assess your choice of trail is the same information you use to judge whether you've reached your target. The information is contained in your *goal.*

It is your goal that keeps you "on target," keeps you from getting sidetracked, helps you decide whether or not you've gone far enough down a particular trail, helps you choose between trails, and tells you when you've reached the target. It is therefore vitally important that you have clearly specified your goal.

Most of the time this is not a problem. We usually know what we're trying to do. Sometimes, however, although we may think we know what we are doing, the goal is fuzzy. If you find a search is becoming more complicated and confusing as you pursue it, the chances are that you need to clarify your goal.

The goal has something to do with the target, and something to do with the starting point (initial recall cue), but it is also something more. For example, say you hear a trumpet, and the trumpet calls to mind a memory of someone singing, and you initiate a search to find out who it is. The trumpet is the initial recall cue; Ella Fitzgerald (though you don't know it at this point) is the target; and the goal could be specified as "a singer I associate with a trumpet," or "a black woman singing along with a famous black jazz trumpeter," or "a black woman singing "they can't take that away from me' with a famous black jazz trumpeter." How specific the goal is depends on how much information is triggered by the initial cue.

The more specific a goal is, the better a guide it will be. Part of the reason for this is that the more specific the goal is, the more information you will have about the target, and therefore the more secondary recall cues you will be able to generate.

Assessing your goal:
⇒ To judge whether you're following the right trail, specify your goal.

⇒ The more specific you can make your goal, the better a guide it will be.

⇒ The more specific your goal, the more information it contains, and therefore the more recall cues it can generate.

⇒ The more specific you can make your goal, the more quickly and accurately you can judge whether you have reached your target.

Exercise 3.3

A. *Goal*: to remember whether you've mailed a check for the car insurance. List the recall cues contained in that statement.

B. *Goal*: to remember whether you mailed a check for the car insurance with the check to the plumber on Monday. List the recall cues contained in that statement.

C. *Goal*: to remember whether you mailed the check for the car insurance with the check to the plumber at the corner mailbox when you walked down after tea on Monday. List the recall cues contained in that statement.

Which goal is most likely to result in you recalling whether or not you mailed the check?

Principles of Retrieving

Memories are codes linked in a network. You need to activate a code to be aware of it. Codes activate each other along the links between them. To find a particular code you must follow along the links between codes.

In theory, any code could be found from any other code, but the "distance" (the number of links) between them may be so great that you would lose interest long before reaching your target. In practice, you need to find a code that is very closely linked to your target. Finding memories is not about your ability to instantly locate target codes, it is about your skill at finding and recognizing codes that are closely linked to the memories you want—codes that are good recall cues.

Whether the initial cue triggers a memory code that is closely linked to your target depends a great deal on context—whether the context in which you are trying to remember the information contains much of the same information as the context in which you originally encoded the information. The less the contexts match, the greater is your need to be skilled at thinking up potential cues. If you have a specific systematic strategy for generating cues in particular circumstances, you will substantially increase your ability to retrieve information.

Principles of retrieving

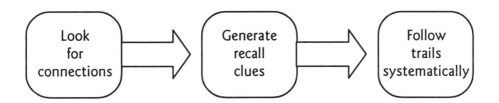

Retrieval strategies

Retrieval strategies are all based on the general principle of systematically generating secondary recall cues. One common strategy is *alphabet search*. In this you try to retrieve a word or name by going through the alphabet to see if any letter triggers any memories. The advantage of this method is that the alphabet provides a foolproof way of ensuring that the potential cues are generated systematically.

Exercise 3.4

To demonstrate the effectiveness of this strategy, look at the following list of countries, covering up the initial letters of the capital cities. Check off those countries for which you immediately know the capital, and check off those for which you are sure you do *not* know the capital. Now, for the remaining items, go systematically through the alphabet looking for the initial letter of the capital city. When you come to a letter that sounds right, write it down, and see if it triggers the name of the capital.

Country	First letter of capital city
Albania	T
Belgium	B
Chile	S
Denmark	C
Equator	Q
Fiji	S
Ghana	A
Hungary	B
Iraq	B
Jamaica	K
Kenya	K
Lebanon	B
Mongolia	U
Nigeria	L
Oman	M
Pakistan	I
Syria	D
Taiwan	T
Uruguay	M
Vietnam	H

Now uncover the initial letters and see how many of the remaining capital cities you can now recall.

Another common retrieval strategy is that of trying to place a person or an event in *time* or *space*. This strategy lacks the formal structure that enables alphabet search to ensure that cues are generated systematically, but a search through time or space does provide constraints that help ensure that cues are neither repeated nor omitted.

If you can remember where you usually see a person or where you have met them before, then you stand a very good chance of retrieving the appropriate memory.

To try to place them, you need to generate possible contexts: the supermarket? the office? the library? the service station? your child's music group? school? friends? And so on. Start with what seems to you to be the most probable places, and then, if necessary, move out to increasingly less probable ones.

To ensure that cues are generated systematically, you need a rule or structure to guide you. A hierarchical category structure can be useful. For example, when searching for the identity of a person, you might develop the following guiding structure:

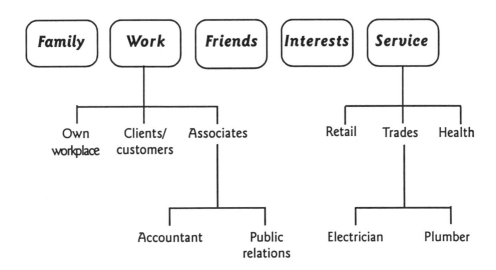

This structure is, of course, emblematic rather than exhaustive. To specify all the types of people you are likely to know would require more space than I have available. You would find it a useful exercise, however, to create your own, rather more specific structure. It's not necessary to go down to the ultimate level of individuals. If you specify the first two levels of your search structure, and in such a way that its organization seems natural to you, you will have created a structure that can guide any future identity search. It will be effective to the extent that it is (a) systematic (prevents you from repeating dead-ends), and (b) exhaustive (if you have "service: health" as a cue, you are unlikely to forget your physiotherapist, but if the category doesn't appear in your search structure, you might well do so).

There appears to be a limit to how many responses can be made to any one cue. An effective generation strategy is therefore one that generates many cues.

8━━🔑

"It's on the tip of my tongue!"

Research suggests that we experience mental blocks (knowing we know something but not able to access it) when we are trying to retrieve information that has not been used for a long time but that we once knew well. This explains why we suffer more memory blocks as we get older—not because our memory Is getting poorer, but because we have more and more information stored away that hasn't been activated for some time.

Although memories that are blocked often seem to come to mind spontaneously hours or even days later, research suggests that you only succeed in retrieving the memory if you keep trying.

If a memory is blocked, you should first use the retrieval strategies to try to generate an appropriate recall cue. If after a minute or so the memory is still blocked, the best thing to do is nothing—let it go. Do something else. After an hour or more, try again.

Successful retrieval requires effective encoding

To find a target memory code, we need to be given or to generate a code that is closely linked to the target. Clearly, the more trails that lead to the target, the greater our chances of finding an effective trail. However, there is a difficulty with this simple rule. All roads may lead to Rome, but if you were heading for Venice *from* Rome, would that help you find the right road? On the contrary, the many roads leading *into* the city would only make it harder to find one particular road *out* of the city.

Here is a simplified portion of a network of memory codes. As you can see, the target code has five links to other memory codes, but each of the five codes that are linked to the target has a different number of links with other memory codes. Clearly, if the memory code with only one link is activated, this will lead readily to the target. If, on the other hand, the code with five links is activated, your chance of initially following the right trail is only one in five.

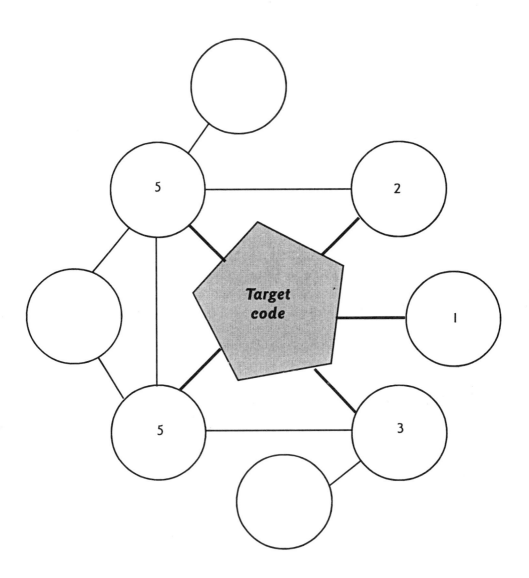

The more potential cues a memory code has (the more codes that are linked to it), the more likely you are to find it. But the more links a cue has, the harder it is to find the right link.

To be easily found, a memory code needs to be strongly linked to a cue that has few other strong links.

An effective retrieval cue:

⇒ Closely matches the target code.

⇒ Contains information that is matched by few other codes in your network.

———

The key to retrieving your memories lies in the way you encoded them. That is why there has been so little work done in designing effective *retrieval* strategies.

Improving your ability to remember is about improving your skill at creating effective memory codes.

Putting it together

Context provides recall cues

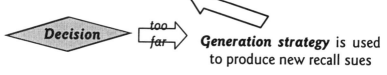

Goal assesses cue's distance from traget

Decision ⟶ too far ⟶ **Generation strategy** is used to produce new recall sues

favorable

Successful retrieval

Main Ideas

- ✆ To find a memory code we follow a trail along the links between the codes.

- ✆ Each trail is signposted by a retrieval cue.

- ✆ The speed of a search depends on the effectiveness of the retrieval cues.

- ✆ A retrieval cue is effective to the extent that strong links connect it with the target memory code.

- ✆ The retrieval cue is more likely to be closely linked to the target code if it contains information that is contained in the code. This is more likely to occur the more the retrieval context matches the encoding context.

- ✆ Your success in finding less accessible memory codes rests on your ability to think of potential retrieval cues.

- ✆ To remember, you need to find the right trail. To find the right trail, you need the right signpost.

Answers to exercises:

3.2

A. Place(s) where you usually mail letters from; other checks you wrote at the same time; any letters you mailed in the past three days; other events on the day you should have mailed it (the day itself is a cue for these).

B. Places where you might know the person from; people with whom the person might be associated.

C. Searching for occasions on which name might have been spoken: occasions you might have played with her; other people who might have been involved; other (social) occasions on which you might have seen her; searching for places name might have appeared in print: club lists, newsletters, etc.

3.3

A. Insurance check; action of mailing.

B. Insurance check; plumber check; action of mailing; Monday.

C. Insurance check; plumber check; action of mailing; corner mailbox; walking to mailbox after tea; Monday.

Goal C is most likely to result in you recalling whether you mailed the check.

3.4

Albania: Tirana; Belgium: Brussels; Chile: Santiago; Denmark: Copenhagen; Ecuador: Quito; Fiji: Suva; Ghana: Accra; Hungary: Budapest; Iraq: Baghdad; Jamaica: Kingston; Kenya: Nairobi; Lebanon: Beirut; Mongolia: Ulan Bator; Nigeria: Lagos; Oman: Muscat; Pakistan: Islamabad; Syria: Damascus; Taiwan: Taipei; Uruguay: Montevideo; Vietnam: Hanoi.

CHAPTER 4
CONNECTION EQUALS UNDERSTANDING

Effective memory codes have strong links with other memory codes. The more strong links a code has, the more easily it will be found. The strength of a link is determined by how often and how recently the link has been activated. The number of links a code has is largely determined by, and determines, your level of understanding. Information is most effectively organized in small, tightly linked clusters, integrated by a single theme, which provides a clear identifying label and a distinctive recall cue.

Making memory codes accessible

An effective memory code is one that is *accessible*.

Our lives are full of the same events, the same people, the same routines. We use our memories constantly and yet for the most part we are unaware of it. Memory codes we use frequently are readily accessible—because we use them frequently. A memory code that is often accessed develops strong links. Every time a link is used it becomes stronger.

The strength of a link is also a function of how long ago it was last used. Even a link that has been used frequently at one time becomes a little rusty if it has not been used for a long while. Similarly, even if a link has only been used once or twice, if it was activated a mere five minutes ago you are unlikely to have any trouble finding it.

The strength of a link then is determined by these two factors: *frequency* of use, and *recency* of use.

The more frequently a code has been activated, the more likely it is to be accessed in the future, because it is called to mind so easily. Which is why our mind develops "ruts"—trails that we can't seem to help following even though we have no particular need to.

**A memory code is strengthened
each time it is activated.**

**A memory code is strengthened by being
linked with frequently activated codes.**

But the accessibility of a code is not only a function of its strength. After all, you have a great many memory codes that are readily available. If strength of the memory code is all that is important, why don't I ever get confused between my fridge and my sofa? Why do I never call my son by the name of our pet rabbit?

But I do sometimes call one son by the name of the other, and I do sometimes call our new rabbit by the name of our previous one. Why are some codes triggered by mistake for others, and why are some codes never confused? Clearly it is a matter of the match between the code and the retrieval cue.

A code readily comes to mind when two factors combine: the code has strong links, and the retrieval cue matches part of the code.

The principles of accessibility:

The accessibility of a memory code is determined by:

⇒ The *frequency effect*: the more often a code has been retrieved, the easier it becomes to find.

⇒ The *recency effect*: a recently retrieved code will be more easily found.

⇒ The *priming effect*: a code will be more easily found if linked codes have just been retrieved.

⇒ The *matching effect*: a code will be more easily found the more the retrieval cue matches the code.

To make a memory code accessible, therefore, you need to link a new code with existing codes that are appropriate (where you would look first) and strong (frequently accessed therefore easily found). The better your linking (more appropriate links, stronger codes, a greater number of strong codes), the more easily you will find that new encoded memory.

For example, to remember the *priming effect*—its name and its meaning—you should not only link it with the other principles of accessibility, but also with information that is already familiar to you and which adds meaning to the new information. There are several, related, uses of the term "to prime" which are relevant to its use in this context: to prime the pump, to prime a firearm, to prime a person. In all of these uses, the meaning is to prepare something or someone so that they are ready for a particular situation.

The priming effect is meaningfully connected to another principle we have looked at earlier: the domino effect. It is also strongly connected with the *recency effect*. If you link the principles that codes trigger other codes (domino effect), and that codes are more easily found when they have been recently retrieved (recency effect), with the definition of priming as to prepare for use, then the priming effect (that a code is primed for activation by the recent activation of other linked codes) is readily understood and remembered.

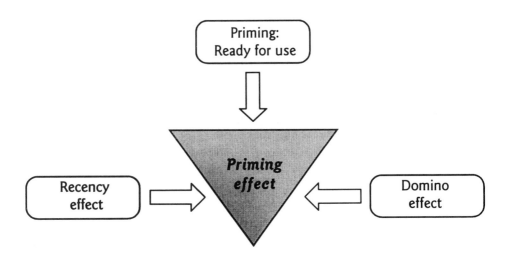

**To make new codes accessible, link them
meaningfully to existing strong codes.**

Priming: an example

⇒ Recognizing a face is easier if you have seen the face earlier.

⇒ Recognition is even easier if you saw it at the same angle, with the same expression.

⇒ Recognition is *not* helped by seeing the *name* earlier.

⇒ Recognition is helped by seeing an associated face (e.g., their partner/child/sibling).

Exercise 4.1

Show the appropriately related items in a similar diagram for the matching effect.

Repetition

To say that links are stronger if they are frequently activated is to make explicit the principle beneath the most common memory strategy of all—so common that we don't even need to be taught it. This strategy is *repetition*.

Although we all know that repetition is important to memory, few of us appreciate the power of even a single repetition. For example, one study found that when people were briefly shown random words to learn, they remembered on average only about 27 percent of words that appeared once compared to 46 percent of words that appeared twice.

Repetition is much more effective if repetitions are separated from each other by other pieces of information. The advantage of spacing occurs with as little as two intervening items between repetitions, but this advantage continues to increase as the interval increases (*spacing effect*).The most effective strategy in fact, is to repeat at increasingly long intervals.

Recall is better if the repetition is spaced.

The spacing effect probably occurs for the same reason that learning something in different contexts increases the likelihood and speed of retrieving the memory—there are more potential retrieval cues. The spacing effect therefore is linked to the context effect and the matching effect.

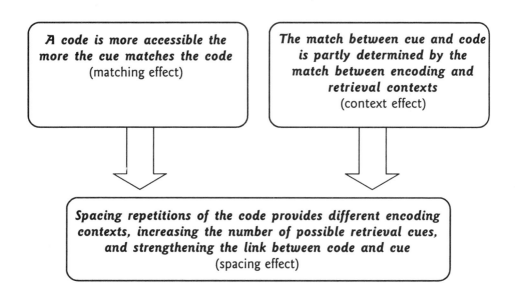

The effectiveness of spaced repetitions is also partly that when repetitions are presented closely together people tend not to pay much attention to the repetition. But they pay *more* attention to later presentations when the presentations are more distant. This agrees with common sense—most of us wouldn't pay much attention to a word being repeated over and over again, but if we were learning a list and an item cropped up again sometime after its first presentation, we would notice it particularly.

Because the spacing effect is a variant of the context effect, you can compensate for a lack of time between repetitions by taking measures to create a change in context. In other words, if you can't space your study of particular material over time, you should try and change the context—either physically (by changing your environment), or by trying to change your mental perspective (much harder).

Connecting and clustering

Making an effective (accessible) memory code involves appropriately connecting the code to existing codes. Effective encoding is therefore about *clustering*. Connecting and clustering give meaning to information.

Clustering examples:

When people are asked to recall specific events that have happened to them, they typically cluster events around a particular theme. Here are two examples (from a study by Barsalou):

1. Went swimming at Red Oaks with a friend of mine
   Went swimming at the University of Hartford because my brother went to summer school there
   Went to the reservoir

2. And we went to Circus World one day
   My brother...brought his girlfriend...I brought my boyfriend...my mom and dad went
   It was really good
   We rode all sorts of rides
   We saw a circus
   We spent most of the day there

Event clusters can be organized around a particular activity (e.g., swimming), or a specific event (going to Circus World), or by time, or place, or the people involved.

Items are clustered together by virtue of the connections between them, by virtue of sharing attributes. The connections between items give meaning to them, but meaning also—and to a greater extent—derives from a *theme*. A meaningful cluster has a theme that unites the components that belong to it. The theme is the glue that holds the cluster together.

For example, if a friend tells you they've bought a new car and it's a Toyota Corolla, you will probably have little trouble remembering the fact of the new car. However, if you have no particular interest in cars, and no special knowledge of that make of car, you are likely to forget the that it is a Toyota Corolla. On the other hand, if you know someone else with a Toyota Corolla, this will provide an additional link which will increase your likelihood of remembering. If two of your friends have that make of car, you will have two links, and your chances of remembering will be even greater.

Look at the following schematic of a memory network.

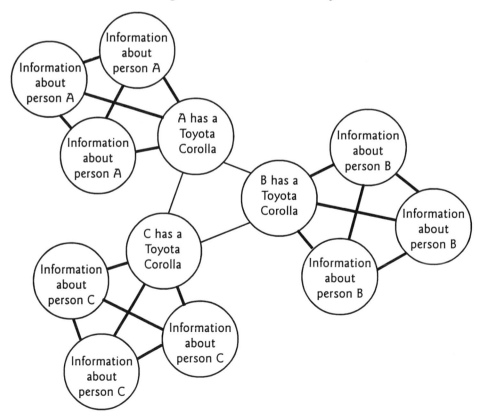

There are three clusters of memory codes, each one representing the information you have encoded for three people. But now with the advent of a new piece of information (C has a Toyota Corolla), the ownership of this particular make of car becomes an item of more interest. Suddenly realizing that three of your friends own a Toyota Corolla, you form links between those memory codes. Ownership of a Toyota Corolla has become more meaningful.

If another piece of information was linked to these codes (maybe something you recently read about this make of car, or your own need to replace your car), then the significance of "Toyota Corolla" would become even greater, and the connected codes may become thematically linked. They become a cluster.

**Information is meaningful to the extent that
its connections give meaning.**

**A cluster is a group of codes linked
by a single theme.**

Principles of effective clustering

In the supermarket, various items are grouped together. Examples of these groups are canned vegetables, fruit and vegetables, dairy products, frozen foods. But not all items clearly belong to a particular group. I never know where to find maple syrup, because, although I would have grouped it with corn syrup, molasses etc, the supermarket puts it with ice cream toppings. This makes no sense to me because I never put maple syrup on ice cream.

This brings us to the first principle of effective clustering:

**Cluster information in a way that makes
sense to you.**

This doesn't mean that you have to do it yourself. Although you probably intuitively feel that if you organize information yourself, you will remember it better than if someone else organizes it for you, this does not seem to be true. It doesn't matter who does the clustering, as long it makes sense to you.

The way you cluster information makes a huge difference to the way you encode it, and to the likelihood of your retrieving it. This is true even in the apparently straightforward exercise of remembering a telephone number. If someone tells you their phone number with a pause after each group of two or three or four digits, this will encourage you to chunk the digits in that way (and is more effective than if the digits are spoken evenly). But if the person then repeats the number, this will help your recall *only if the pauses are in the same place.*

In other words, 528-3467 is a completely different number from 52-83-467.

Themes integrate clusters, labels articulate themes

To help customers find items in a supermarket, aisles are labeled with the categories of items stored there. These labels may be considered as the themes that encapsulate the important shared attribute of the members of the group. As long as the labels successfully encapsulate that common attribute, the labeling will be successful. But of course, as we all know from personal experience, the labels are not always successful.

Why not? Because the supermarket understandably wants to limit the number of category labels on the signs, and the broader your category, the less likely it is that all members of that category will clearly and unambiguously share one common attribute. To be able to label a cluster effectively, the cluster needs to be narrowly focused.

Only include information that is tightly linked in the same cluster.

Ask yourself, can you come up with a word or brief phrase that applies to each of the bits of information within the cluster? If not, the cluster is not sufficiently tightly linked. It contains information that doesn't belong.

The more specific the theme is, the more effective it will be. The degree to which the codes in a cluster are connected to each other is reflected in the specificity of the theme.

Look at the following set of statements (taken from a study by Cantor and Engle):

1. The teacher took a table near a window.

2. The teacher read the menu.

3. The teacher asked for a glass of water.

4. The teacher checked his wallet.

5. The teacher munched on a breadstick.

6. The teacher placed an order.

Compare these statements with the following set:

1. The teacher took a table near a window.

2. The teacher read the menu.

3. The teacher found that the prices were high.

4. The teacher checked his wallet.

5. The teacher decided he could afford a steak.

6. The teacher placed an order.

Both sets of statements may be regarded as being related by the theme "having a meal at a restaurant." But the two different sentences in the second set increase the integration of the statements dramatically. This increase in the number and strength of the connections between the statements of the set is reflected in the more specific theme of the second set: "the cost of going out for a meal."

If you learned the information in these two sets of statements, and were then asked questions about them, you would take longer to retrieve information from the first set of statements. If more statements were added to the sets, it would take even longer to retrieve information from the first set—because each statement would need to be activated and checked (the *fan effect*). However, retrieving information from the second set of statements would not be slowed by the number of statements in the set—as long as the statements were tightly linked.

> **The greater the number of linked codes
> that a code has, the longer it takes
> to retrieve that code.**

> **But a code in a cluster takes
> less time to retrieve, even when the cluster
> contains many codes.**

Limit amount of information in the cluster

Although it is easier to retrieve a code when it is in a cluster, people tend to recall only about five items from one cluster. It's a good idea, therefore, to break information into more clusters rather than less. For example, if you had 40 items to remember, around 25 items would be remembered if you learned them as five groups of eight items, but all of them might be remembered if you had put them into eight groups of five.

> **The number of clusters used affects how much
> is remembered.**

> **More, smaller groups are better than fewer,
> larger groups.**

The clusters serve as secondary recall cues—which is why, to be effective, they need some sort of identifying label. This label usually encapsulates the theme. The label *anchors* the codes in a cluster.

> **Clusters need a unique identifying label that
> encapsulates the theme.**

Build super-clusters

Clustering on its own helps connect only the information within a cluster. We also need to connect the clusters. One cluster must lead to another. Thus, if you have a list of 40 items to learn and you have divided it into eight clusters of five, you would ideally like any one of those eight labels (retrieval cues) to trigger all other clusters. If, indeed, you managed to build strong connections between *all* the clusters, you would have built a *super-cluster*.

The more connections we can make between different clusters, the more integrated the network of clusters will be, and the more meaningful the information will be. Remember, it is the connections between information that give it meaning. And it is the connections—their number and strength—that make memory codes accessible.

A super-cluster has many potential retrieval cues; information in a super-cluster is readily accessible; and a super-cluster is treated as a single item. This is why the fan effect (slow retrieval when too many paths lead into and out of the memory code) doesn't apply to codes in a super-cluster.

Make as many links between clusters as you can.

Why does an expert learn new information so easily?

One of the characteristics of experts is that they can acquire new information in their subject much more easily than a novice. The reason for this is that an expert's memory has a strong framework— a tightly linked network of super-clusters.

Moreover, an expert's clusters and super-clusters usually have deeper anchors. Typically, a novice clusters information on the basis of superficial similarities, whereas an expert builds clusters around meaningful principles and relationships.

Patterns of connection

It's a well-established fact that organizing information in a hierarchical or linear arrangement improves recall, but organizing information in a matrix can be even more effective. Compare the following examples showing items organized in (a) a hierarchical arrangement, and (b) a matrix structure (example taken from a study by Broadbent, Cooper and Broadbent):

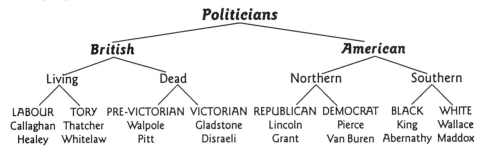

Politicians

	Before 1900		After 1900	
	British	*American*	*British*	*American*
A-L	Gladstone Disraeli	Lincoln Grant	Callaghan Healey	King Abernathy
M-Z	Walpole Pitt	Pierce Van Buren	Thatcher Whitelaw	Wallace Maddox

Both these ways of organizing information dramatically improve recall compared to a mere list of items, but the matrix arrangement has an advantage in that there are more retrieval paths to the items. Thus, for example, if you forgot the retrieval cue "tory" (in the hierarchical arrangement), you would be unable to access Thatcher and Whitelaw. But if you forgot the cue M-Z, you might still access Thatcher and Whitelaw through "British."

Reflecting the greater number of retrieval paths, a matrix also demonstrates more connections than a hierarchical structure. If you study the names of politicians in the hierarchical tree, the only items that are transparently linked are the paired names. However, if you study the matrix, the connections between, say, Gladstone and Disraeli, and Walpole and Pitt are very obvious.

Six rules of effective clustering:

1. Cluster information in a way that makes sense to you.
2. Only include information that is tightly linked in the same cluster.
3. More, smaller clusters are better than fewer, larger clusters.
4. Give each cluster an identifying label.
5. Connect tightly integrated clusters with related clusters.
6. Make as many connections between clusters as you can.

The key to memory lies in setting up good retrieval cues. The important question thus becomes, not "how do I get a good memory?", but "how can I best organize this material to provide a rich set of potential recall cues so that it is easy to remember?"

Organize material to provide a rich set of potential recall cues.

Organize material to form a tightly integrated network.

Exercise 4.1

Here is a set of statements about the life of Antonio Vivaldi, composer of the *Four Seasons*:

1. He was born in Venice in 1678, on the day of an earthquake.

2. He was the eldest of eight children, and the only one to become a musician.

3. His father was a professional violinist.

4. He was ordained a priest in 1703.

5. His first official post was as a violin master.

6. He had red hair, and was nicknamed "the red priest."

7. He ceased to say Mass not long after his ordination.

8. He lost part of his income through his failure to say Mass.

9. He blamed his failure to say Mass on an ailment he had suffered from childhood (possibly asthma).

10. In 1737 he was censured for conduct unbecoming to a priest.

11. He was refused entry to Ferrara on the grounds of his supposed relationship with a singer and his refusal to say Mass.

12. Although he had composed many pieces, which had been very popular and well-paid, he died in poverty.

Which of these statements are connected? Can you form any clusters, where each statement is connected with every other statement, and whose shared connections can be encapsulated in a single theme? What is the theme (in a word or phrase)?

Now close the book and see how many statements you can recall (for meaning, not verbatim). You should find that statements you have linked with others are easier to recall than isolated statements, and that clustered statements are much easier to recall.

Putting it together

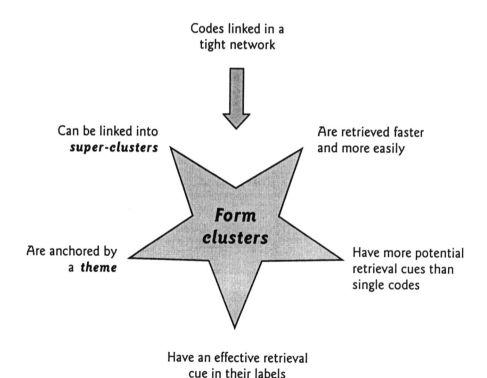

Codes linked in a
tight network

Can be linked into
super-clusters

Are retrieved faster
and more easily

**Form
clusters**

Are anchored by
a **theme**

Have more potential
retrieval cues than
single codes

Have an effective retrieval
cue in their labels

Main Ideas

❧ Memory codes are easily accessed when they have strong links.

❧ Links are strengthened by being used frequently.

❧ Some activation remains in an activated link for a time, making it easier to re-activate.

❧ To encode new information so that it will be accessible, you need to connect it meaningfully with existing strong codes.

❧ Repeating information strengthens its code, but repeating it at spaced intervals, in different contexts, increases the number and strength of its links.

❧ The links between codes make them meaningful, but meaning is greater when a single theme integrates linked codes.

❧ To ensure linked codes are integrated by a single theme, and to provide a retrieval cue, clusters should have an identifying label.

❧ The more strong links there are between codes in a cluster, the more likely it is to be treated as a single unit, facilitating recall of all the information contained in it.

❧ The more links between codes, the more potential recall cues.

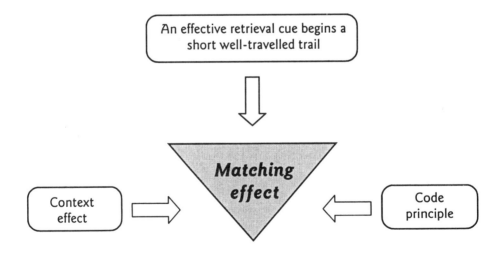

🔑━━

Answers to exercises:

4.1

There are connections between 3 and 5, 4 and 6, 7 and 8 and 9, 7 and 10; 7 and 11, 10 and 11, 8 and 12.

You could form a cluster with 7 and 8 and 9 and 10 and 11 around the theme *Vivaldi's failure as a priest*.

———

Chapter 5

Selecting the Right Information

The information you select for inclusion in your memory code determines how the code connects to other codes. The information selected and the connections made determines how many potential recall cues a code will have, and how effective they will be. Items that need to be memorized rather than learned will not have the rich network of potential cues that well-understood meaningful information has. The selection of other codes that can be connected to such items imposes meaning and thus aids recall.

Selection governs connection

Memory codes are selected bits of information. The links that connect a code with other codes—and consequently the retrieval cues that will be effective—depend on what bits of information have been selected.

Much of the reason why some people have a "good" memory and others have a "bad" one lies in the different ways people encode information. What aspects are selected for encoding? What aspects are rejected? What governs the selection?

Similarity joins and distinctiveness separates

One very important rule guiding our selection is that we look for features that are shared by as few other items as possible (the *distinctiveness principle*). This is in keeping with our principle of choosing effective retrieval cues (an effective retrieval cue contains information that is matched by few other codes in your network).

The selection of these distinctive features is guided by context.

For example, the image of a girl doing a handstand would be distinctive in an advertisement for office furniture, but unremarkable in the context of a gymnastics display. If the girl was dressed in a suit, this would be distinctive whatever the context, but if the viewer's own small child was also in the scene this might well overwhelm even such a bizarre sight as a girl in a suit doing a handstand.

Distinctiveness is not only relative, but also subjective.

Distinctiveness is personal.

Distinctiveness depends on context.

We are all familiar with the way distinctive smells can recall particular memories. I myself always remember my grandmother when I smell Christmas lilies, because whenever we arrived for Christmas at her house she would have them arranged on the hall table, and their distinctive fragrance would fill the hall.

A study that looked at the effects of odor on memory found that information learned in the presence of novel smells was remembered better if the smell was available during retrieval. If the smell was a familiar one, a contextually inappropriate smell (in this study, peppermint) was a better recall cue than an appropriate one (pine).

You can reduce distinctiveness by concentrating on some highly general information. For example, in a list of words you could focus on the number of times the letter "e" appears. In such circumstances you are less likely to notice any distinctive words (such as "computer" among a list of fruits). However, if the word is structurally distinctive ("phlegm," for example, has an unusual sequence of letters giving it a distinctive shape), it is likely to be *more* easily remembered in a situation where you are concentrating on a very general aspect.

Similarly, you increase distinctiveness, and therefore your chance of remembering, when you focus on an aspect of an item that distinguishes it from the surrounding item. For example, in a list of fruit, "banana" is not likely to stand out. However, if you are specifically picking out fruit that start with a "b," "banana" will be more distinctive.

Distinctiveness can be manipulated by selective attention.

If "banana" is encoded simply as a "common fruit," then it will be harder to find among all the other common fruit than if it is coded under "common fruit that starts with 'b.'" If it is coded as "common fruit that starts with 'b' and is yellow" it will be even easier to find. When encoding an item you need enough information to distinguish that item from all the other items already stored. The more specific the code, the quicker and easier it will be found.

Recall improves as the code becomes more specific.

Hence, if you're trying to think of the name of a fruit, you will be better off if you know its starting letter, better still if you remember that it repeated itself, and best of all if you remember it had something to do with a cat's foot (pawpaw).

Choose distinctive features that uniquely specify the concept. The more distinctive, the easier found.

Essentially you are looking for features (bits of a code) that will be good retrieval cues. These may even be fragments of an item.

Say you wanted to remember the name of a company called Computer Cable Services. You might simply repeat the whole name a few times to yourself and hope that it will just pop up when you need it. But this is not particularly likely to be successful if you have not paid any special attention to the individual words. The first word, "computer," is too common to serve as a good recall cue, and this is the one you are likely to have paid most attention to, simply because it is first. If, however, you marked "cable" as the least common term in the company's name and made a special effort to remember that, you are far more likely to be successful in remembering the name. When you try to retrieve the name, if you have been successful in remembering that one word (cable), then this cue is not likely to be linked with many other items, and the link to Computer Cable Services is likely to be the most recent and consequently easily accessed. "Cable" has provided an anchor for "Computer Cable Services."

The fragment being used as a recall cue need not be a whole word. Part of a word may well serve as a good cue. For example, you might pick out "hypo" or "thyroid" to help you remember the medical term "hypothyroidism." Which fragment will be the better recall cue depends on you—whichever you find more distinctive.

Distinctive cues anchor the code.

How easily a code is retrieved depends on:
⇒ The number of potential targets that can be generated.
⇒ How easily the target code can be distinguished from other potential targets.

Exercise 5.1
Look back at the details you recalled about the life of Vivaldi. Were there any details that were trivial in themselves, but that you recalled because they were unusual or interesting? Did recall of these details cue you to remembrance of more significant linked items?

Principles of Encoding

Distinctive bits are vital to help you find a code among all the other codes in your memory, but, as we discussed in the previous chapter, making connections is even more critical. In making connections we don't look for differences, but for similarities.

Principles of Encoding

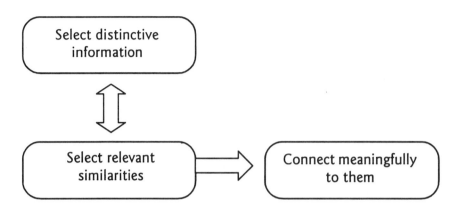

The key to memory lies in setting up good retrieval cues. Partly this involves selecting useful bits of information, partly this involves making connections between codes. In the previous chapter I spoke of the importance of integrating codes into a tightly linked cluster with its own unique identity. Such a cluster can be treated as a single unit, benefiting speed and ease of retrieval (the super-cluster effect). But some information is not readily integrated. Such information must be memorized rather than learned.

Rote-learning of unrelated material

Memorizing versus learning

We commonly distinguish between learning by rote—memorizing —and 'true' learning. For most of us, memorizing is a matter of brute force. The principal tool is simple repetition. You recite the information over and over and over again, until you have pounded it into your brain. It works—I can still recite a piece from *A Midsummer's Night Dream* that I learned by this method one dreary Sunday afternoon about 25 years ago—but it is hard work, and, of course, very boring.

Memorizing is what we do when we need to remember the exact words, as in the following situations:

- ◆ Memorizing words from a foreign language.

- ◆ Memorizing speeches, poems, etc.

- ◆ Memorizing names and faces.

- ◆ Memorizing a shopping list.

- ◆ Memorizing phone numbers.

But, of course, in most situations we only need to remember the sense of the information.

True learning requires understanding, and that comes from the connections between codes. In one sense it is harder work than memorization, because you must think, you must dig for the connections. Memorization is boring and time-consuming, but it is not difficult as such. However, true learning builds on itself. If you put the effort into understanding material you find difficult, you will reap your reward in the long-term. Later information will be acquired more easily. It will "slot in" to your existing framework. Memorization, on the other hand, doesn't build on itself. It is just as difficult to memorize a related text as it was to memorize the first text.

In materials without inherent structure, organization must be forced on the information. To aid recall, meaning is imposed on the information by selecting and connecting meaningful codes to the material to be memorized. The selection of information is thus quite different for material that is not organized around a theme.

Principles of effective selection

Meaningful material is remembered better than meaningless material

We all know that meaningless strings of words or numbers are hard to learn. Telephone numbers, for example, usually begin with digits that reflect the area the telephone is in, and go on to list digits that simply reflect when the telephone was connected. If you are familiar with the area code, then the first digits have some meaning to you and are therefore easier to remember. However the last digits appear completely random and are accordingly much more difficult to learn.

In this situation, there are two common strategies. Either we try to find some sort of pattern or meaning in the digits, or, if we only want to remember the number long enough to dial it or write it down, we continuously repeat it to ourselves. Although simple repetition is adequate when we only need to remember something for a few minutes, the information will slip away as soon as we stop repeating it.

We do of course remember phone numbers that we use frequently. This is because of the sheer number of times the information is activated (strengthening the code) and because the repetition is spaced.

Acquiring a phone number this way takes time, however. A more effective and quicker strategy is to add meaning. The use of letters on telephones to encode the digits enables phone numbers to be transformed into words: 1-800-CALL-ATT is much more meaningful and easier to remember than 1-800-225-5288.

Meaningless does not mean random. While telephone numbers may be arbitrary, we cannot say that a sonnet is a random arrangement of words. The distinction I make between information that is meaningful and information that is meaningless is not a distinction between sense and nonsense, but a distinction depending on whether your goal is to understand or to parrot.

Where understanding is your goal, clustering and meaningful connections between codes is all-important. But where your goal is to be able to reproduce the information verbatim, the emphasis is on forcing links with strong codes, to establish better retrieval cues.

The transformation of meaningless information into meaningful information, either through direct transformation or indirectly through connections with meaningful codes, is the basis of mnemonic strategies of all kinds (discussed at length in chapter 10).

To learn meaningless material, make it meaningful.

Concrete words make better recall cues

When memorizing meaningless information, the more concrete the recall cues, the better it will be remembered.

It is well-established that words that refer to concrete, easily visualized objects are remembered better than words that refer to abstract concepts (for example, "justice," "love"). This is because concrete words are particularly effective as recall cues.

Concrete words seem to have many more links to other codes than abstract concepts and so concrete words are far more easily associated with meaningless material.

Choose concrete words as recall cues

Concreteness may be defined in terms of how easy it is to form a mental image of the concept. In a situation where it is hard to produce images (for example, when words are presented very briefly and quickly, or when the person is unaware she needs to try to remember the material), the advantage of concrete words over abstract words is much less.

Moreover, if people are told to form images there is no difference between the learning of abstract and concrete words. It appears then that concrete words are usually remembered better because concrete words are more easily visualized than abstract words. The rule for choosing concrete words is therefore more accurately expressed as:

Choose easily visualized recall cues.

Interaction is the key to the effectiveness of imagery

The effectiveness of *imagery* is well-established. One study found that forming mental images was more than twice as effective as simply repeating the material (the most basic strategy). But imagery is most effective when interacting or *relational images* are used. Indeed interaction is in large part the key to the effectiveness of imagery. For example, if you had to memorize the words: "cat" "drum" "broom" and "table," you would be better to make one image of, say, a cat sweeping a table with a drum balanced on his head, rather than four different images.

When learning unrelated material, create relational images.

But items may be related to one another through words as well as by images. One way of relating items verbally is by making up a story. For example, here is a brief story to help memorize a shopping list of ten items (the items are capitalized): "the BREAD is full of JUICE. I will MILK it and wash the PAPER TOWEL off, then FISH for CORN, CHIP it into BEANS and STOCK up on ORANGES."

The use of this strategy has a dramatic effect on rote-learning, compared to the use of a simple strategy such as repetition.

Although imagery is propounded by many memory trainers as the secret to memory improvement, there is not in fact anything particularly miraculous about imagery. Verbal associations can be equally effective retrieval cues. The advantage of visual images is quite simply that it is often easier to make connections between codes by visualizing them together than by connecting them with words. On the other hand, many people find it difficult to create images.

The key to remembering unrelated material is in forming relationships between the concepts. This can be done through mental images, or through words. Pick which one you are more comfortable with.

Link unrelated material through words or
im ages.

Other types of good recall cues

Some words by their very nature are easier to remember than other words, and so provide particularly good recall cues:

- •◆ Words that look odd (e.g., phlegm).

- •◆ Words that sound or look similar (e.g., sound–hound; foreman–human).

- •◆ Common words that are required to be pronounced in an uncommon way (e.g., colonel, ache, one, two, knee, aisle).

Features to look for in a recall cue:
⇒ Easily visualized items.

⇒ Synonyms.

⇒ Rhymes.

⇒ Words that are unusual in looks or sound.

⇒ Memorable fragments of the item.

Exercise 5.3

Look again at the list of statements about Vivaldi in the previous chapter. Pick out the details that you consider distinctive. Consider the connections you made—can you form new links by emphasizing the distinctive details?

Now see how many details you can recall about Vivaldi.

To remember meaningless material:

•• Make it more meaningful.

•• Use words or images to link it with more meaningful codes.

•• Link it with codes that will be good recall cues.

Attention matters

Encoding can occur without intention, without effort. But to encode well, you need to pay attention.

If you divide your attention when encoding information you markedly reduce your memory for that information. Dividing your attention when trying to remember has much less impact on your ability to retrieve information—retrieval is a much more automatic process than encoding. After all, retrieval simply involves following a marked trail, but encoding involves selecting the information to be encoded, and connecting it with related information.

Effective encoding needs well-directed attention.

Attention is not synonymous with effort. To say that someone works hard is not the same as saying that they work well. Working hard refers mainly to the number of hours spent. Working well refers to an outcome.

Effort alone doesn't produce good learning. We are all familiar with people who never seem to work hard at studying but do well at exams, and people who work, work, work, and still do poorly. This is not simply a matter of one being "smarter" than the other. You can try as hard as you like, but if you are using the wrong learning strategy for that particular task, then the information will not be well encoded (that is, encoded to maximize easy retrieval).

But you can minimize time spent by using appropriate learning strategies and applying the principles of learning. An hour of concentrated, well-directed learning is worth several hours of misdirected or poorly attended effort.

Well-directed attention reduces learning time.

Of course the trick is in knowing where to direct your attention. The essence of knowing where to focus lies in remembering and applying the fundamentals of encoding/retrieving. Namely, create good potential retrieval cues, by selecting distinctive information and forming appropriate and strong links. The role of attention is to improve your chances of achieving these goals.

Putting it together

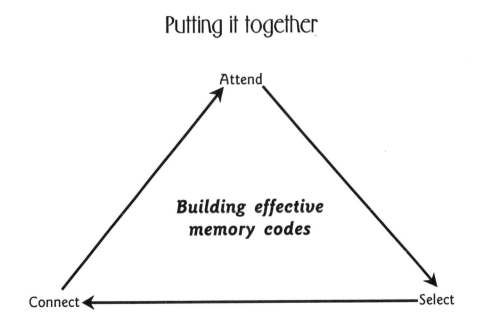

73

Main Ideas

ᴄᴣ The connections we make depend on what information we have selected to encode.

ᴄᴣ To integrate information we focus on shared attributes (similarity), but to select useful links we must focus on distinctive features.

ᴄᴣ Distinctiveness is relative and personal, and can be manipulated by selective attention.

ᴄᴣ The more specific a code is, the easier it will be to find.

ᴄᴣ To encode effectively, your attention needs to be focused on selecting distinctive information and forming appropriate and strong connections.

ᴄᴣ Memorization requires information to be either transformed into, or to be linked with, more meaningful information.

CHAPTER 6
THE WORKING MEMORY

To create an effective memory code, you need to attend to the information and select and understand what you want to remember. Your ability to do this is limited by how many memory codes you can work with at one time. Accordingly, you need to know your own capabilities and learn to work within your limits.

Obviously encoding occurs before the information is permanently stored. There must be a stage, a state of mind, in which the information is considered and selected. This state of mind is called *working memory*. The working memory holds the information you are working on.

Working memory contains the information of which you are immediately aware.

To "remember" something, we have to retrieve it from our memory store and transform it into a working memory code—only then can we know what we have found. We call this making information *active*.

To activate information is to transform it into a working memory code.

Material that has been well learned will have a stronger memory code, and so can be more quickly activated (brought into conscious awareness).

Encoding refers to the transformation of information from a working memory code into a database code.

Retrieving involves the transformation of information from a database code into a working memory code.

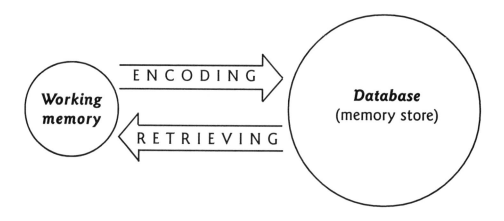

Interaction between working memory and the database

Older books talk of these two states (working memory and the database) as if they were different places—as if there were a table on which your papers are spread out (working memory) and a roomful of filing cabinets from which more files can be taken out (the database). It's a useful analogy, of course, but the relationship between working memory and the database is more fluid than this. You don't have to clear some space on the table (working memory is a very small work space), trudge over to the cabinets, search for the next file you want, bring it back to the table, look at it, discover you need something else as well, make more room on the table (by picking up the papers and taking them with you to the cabinets and filing them), and get the next file out of the cabinet.

Memory theories today suggest that working memory and the database are not separately located memory *stores*, operating in different ways, but that they are different memory *processes* that create or *transform* memory codes.

It is therefore somewhat misleading when we talk of information being "in" working memory or "in" the database. More accurately, we should say that information is in a working memory code (that is, an active code) or in a database code (a stored, passive code).

This is not just a matter of academic pedantry. Because working memory and the database are not completely separate entities, they can interact in a way which increases the capacity of working memory, and so increases the amount of information you can work on at one time. Instead of a small table and a roomful of files, we have a theater and a moving spotlight. The spotlight can grow or shrink, be a wide, diffused light or a tight, focused light.

In one regard, however, this analogy breaks down. Every time we relate our database to something in the outside world—an office, a library, a theater—we have the same fundamental problem. In the world outside our mind, things have their place. A book and a lamp on a table beside a chair will stay a book and a lamp on a table beside a chair until and unless someone moves them. But the memories in your head dance.

The codes in the spotlight do not therefore have to be sitting together in the theatre. Imagine them instead in a ballroom. The codes waltz around the dance floor. Here two couples are dancing close together, there two couples change partners. The spotlight moves, its very action bringing about changes in the dancers. "Quick," they say, hurrying over to get in the spotlight. In response to the dancers, the spotlight too changes. It thinks, "Oh, look at that arrangement," and it grows larger, more diffuse, to catch it all.

Some people have a better spotlight than others. It is more flexible, more responsive to the needs of the moment. It has a greater capacity to grow and illuminate more of the dancers at a time.

Your working memory capacity (how much information you can work with at one time) is a critical factor in determining your ability to take good notes, read efficiently, understand complex issues, reason. Indeed, it may be your working memory capacity that best "measures" your intelligence.

Some people, of course, are born with a capacious, flexible working memory. But it is not like eye color—an attribute predetermined by your genes and incapable of being modified. You can increase your working memory capacity. To do so, it helps to understand how working memory works, and how it interacts with the database.

How we use working memory

Reading comprehension

Consider these two sentences: The spy quickly threw his report in the fire. The ashes floated up the chimney.

Perfectly comprehensible, yes? But the second sentence doesn't actually follow on directly from the first, unless you realize (as you assuredly did) that (a) the report was on paper, and (b) paper turns to ash in fire. Now I don't suppose you were aware of making those connections when reading those two sentences. We have a vast fund of knowledge that is so readily accessible that we don't have to think about it. Nevertheless, even though we are not aware of it, the knowledge still has to be accessed from memory.

Those two sentences were taken from an experimental study that looked at how people vary in their ability to fill in the missing connections. Clearly your ability to understand what you're reading or hearing depends to some extent on your skill at filling in the missing gaps. That skill probably depends on two main factors:

- How much information you can keep active at one time.

- How quickly you can access the relevant information from your database.

Exercise 6.1

Read the following passages and answer the comprehension questions about them, without referring back to the text. (Text and questions are taken from an experimental study by Daneman and Carpenter).

1. Sitting with Richie, Archie, Walter and the rest of the gang in the Grill yesterday, I began to feel uneasy. Robbie had put a dime in the juke box. It was blaring one of the latest rock 'n roll favorites. I was studying, in horror, the reactions of my friends to the music. I was especially perturbed by the expression on my best friend's face. Wayne looked intense and was pounding the table furiously to the beat. Now, I like most of the things other teenage boys like. I like girls with soft blonde hair, girls with dark curly hair, in fact all girls. I like milkshakes, football games and beach parties. I like denim jeans, fancy T-shirts and sneakers. It is not that I dislike rock music but I think it is supposed to be fun and not taken too seriously. And here he was, "all shook up" and serious over the crazy music.

   Who was "all shook up" and serious over the music?

2. It was midnight and the jungle was very still. Suddenly the cry of a wolf pierced the air. This anguished note was followed by a flurry of activity. All the beasts of the jungle recognized that an urgent meeting had been summoned by the lion, their king. Representatives from each species made rapid preparations to get to the river clearing. This was where all such emergency assemblies were held. The elephant and tiger were the first to arrive. Next came the gorilla, panther and snake. They were following by the owl and the crocodile. The proceedings were delayed because the leopard had not shown up yet. There was much speculation as to the reasons for the midnight alarm. Finally he arrived and the meeting could commence.

   Who finally arrived?

In both passages, to understand the agent in the final sentence you must remember the reference in an earlier sentence. In the latter passage, this reference is only two sentences earlier, but in the first passage, the reference is six sentences back.

Readers with a low capacity for information of this type have difficulty with a reference more than two or three sentences back.

Mental arithmetic

Doing sums in your head requires you to have a store of well-learned sums and products (6+7=13; 3x3=9; and so on). These might be considered the alphabet of arithmetic calculation. When attempting to calculate, say, 45+32, you will use the known sums of 4+3 and 5+2. But you also need to remember the first 7 while you retrieve the second 7, and that's where working memory is needed.

Many errors in mental arithmetic occur because the person has failed to hold all the partial solutions in working memory. Remembering one 7 while you retrieve a second 7 doesn't seem very hard, but what about a problem like 4735 + 629? You have to hold in working memory not only each retrieved sum (5+9, 3+2, 7+6) but also the carried amounts. And of course, you must remember not only the values of the sums, but also their order.

> **Your working memory capacity is critical in determining your skill at understanding, thinking and calculating.**

Exercise 6.2:

Find some way of meaningfully relating the digits in these three different chunking patterns (suggestions at the end of the chapter).

Differences between working memory and database codes

Working memory codes and database codes have typical characteristics associated with them. These characteristics are not absolutely associated with one code rather than another. However, knowledge of these characteristics will help you understand how these different processes work.

Working memory codes and database codes have the following characteristics:

- Information in working memory tends to be encoded in terms of its sound (an *acoustic* code).

- Information in the database tends to be recorded in terms of its meaning (a *semantic* code).

- Information in working memory can only be maintained there as long as you are aware of it.

- Information in the database is maintained without your attention, but it may be difficult to retrieve because of interference from other memory codes.

- The capacity of working memory is limited.

- The capacity of the database is in practice unlimited.

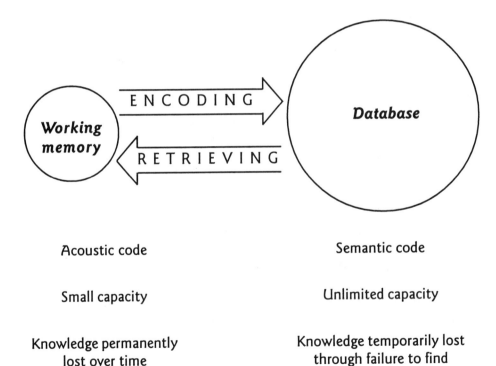

Acoustic code	Semantic code
Small capacity	Unlimited capacity
Knowledge permanently lost over time	Knowledge temporarily lost through failure to find

Holding information in working memory

What are the practical implications of these differences between the working memory and the database?

Probably the most important difference between active working memory codes and passive database codes is the way in which the codes are maintained. A memory code in its passive stored state is maintained effortlessly. It may be destroyed by physical damage; it may become corrupted by later amendments; it may become hard to find by not being retrieved for many years. But it is maintained without your conscious attention. The capacity of your database, your success in finding particular memory codes and their resistance to corruption or damage all depend, as pointed out in previous chapters, on one major factor—organization.

An active working memory code, however, is a temporary state which cannot be maintained for more than a few seconds without conscious attention. It is this which so limits working memory capacity.

Maintenance rehearsal

Information is held in working memory through rehearsal; that is, by repeating the information over and over again to ourselves. Most of us use this strategy when we are given a phone number and we just want to hold it in our minds long enough to write it down, or call the number. We are all familiar with the ease with which this information is lost as soon as something or someone interrupts us.

The name for this process is *maintenance rehearsal* (rehearsal to maintain information in working memory). Usually, repeating to oneself in this way is only sufficient to hold the information for as long as you are rehearsing it. As soon as you stop, the information is gone.

It is this need for your attention that limits the capacity of working memory. You can only hold as much as you can attend to at one time. It's like juggling. As long as you keep the balls moving you're fine, but once the number of balls increases to the point where you lose track of one or more balls, you're sunk. The balls come tumbling down. The information is lost.

Some people are better jugglers than others. But like most things, it's a matter of practice, not simply native ability.

There are, of course, defined physical limits on the number of balls it is possible to juggle, no matter how much practice you have. Expert jugglers don't amaze by juggling 30 balls, they amaze by changing the nature of what they juggle. Juggling five fiery torches is more impressive than juggling five balls. Similarly, although you can slightly increase your working memory capacity by increasing your ability to attend to a number of different things at once, you will have a much greater effect by changing the nature of your information chunks.

Chunk, although it doesn't sound like it, is the technical term for the bits of information that working memory works with. Chunks are the juggling balls.

Chunking

A chunk is any unit of information organized according to some rule or pattern.

Probably the most widely known fact about working memory is that it can only hold around seven chunks of information (between five and nine). However, this tells us little about the limits of working memory because the size of a chunk is indeterminate.

For example, if you have to remember a phone number, each digit might represent a chunk. Say the number is 478-6923. If you treat each digit as a separate piece of information, as when you simply repeat it, remembering the phone number (seven digits) takes up all your working memory capacity, and you have no attention to spare for anything else until you have finished with the number. However, if you want to remember the number for a long time, then you might try to find something about the relationship between the digits to make it easier to remember. You could divide it into three chunks: 478, 69, 23. Or two: 478, 6923. If you related all the digits to each other, the seven-digit phone number would become one chunk.

A chunk may be thought of as a pronounceable label—it is, after all, a type of cluster, and the extent to which it can be treated as an integrated unit is determined by whether it can be given a single label.

What governs the size of a chunk is meaningfulness. And meaningfulness is quite personal. What has meaning for me will not necessarily have any meaning for you.

How chunking increases the amount of information you can hold:

People can usually repeat back four nonsense syllables, such as
   SUG KOL FEK GIX

but not six:
   RYN DEQ CUX GYT POB VED

They can repeat back six one-syllable words:
   CAT DOG RAM HIT LAW FIG

but not nine one-syllable words:
   LOG HAT DIM RUN TIN POT WAX SUN LIP

They can repeat back three four-syllable words (equaling 12 syllables):
   DICTIONARY ILLUSTRIOUS RESPONSIBLE CORONATION

but not six four-syllable words:
   CHAMELEON DROMEDARY DUPLICATION MECHANISM
   EVOLUTION STATISTICAL

But they can repeat back a nineteen word sentence!
   MATERIAL THAT HAS BEEN WELL LEARNED WILL BE MORE
   STRONGLY ENCODED, AND THUS IT CAN BE MORE QUICKLY
   ACTIVATED.

**A chunk is any organized unit of information
that has meaning for you.**

**Chunking increases the amount of
information you can hold in working memory.**

I have discussed this as if it is critically the *number* of chunks that determines whether your work space is full. However, some recent research has suggested that the limiting factor is actually the time it takes you to say the words. It appears that you can only hold in working memory what you can say in 1.5—2 seconds. Slow speakers are therefore penalized.

The importance of verbal rehearsal is, of course, because working memory codes are usually sound-based.

Of course not all information can be expressed in an acoustic code. Some, for example, may be expressed in images. There may indeed be a number of different working spaces: one for material that is heard, one for material that is seen, one for material that is smelt, one for material that is felt, etc. At this stage, little is known about the way information from senses other than ears and eyes is processed.

When maintenance rehearsal helps long-term recall:

Simple repetition can help you *recognize* information.

Simple repetition doesn't usually help *recall*, because:

⇒ It maintains items in a speech (acoustic) code.

⇒ It doesn't form links with potential semantic retrieval cues.

⇒ Simple repetition can assist recall when:

⇒ Acoustic information is a distinctive part of the memory code, *and*

⇒ You use acoustic cues in your generation strategy.

Determining your working memory capacity

Because there are several different components within working memory, there is no single measure of working memory capacity. Your capacity for numbers may well be quite different from your capacity for words, and both may be different from your capacity for visual images.

Digit span

This refers to the number of digits that you can correctly repeat back, in the correct order. To measure your digit span, refer to the appendix at the end of the book. A normal, unpracticed, person has a digit span of between four and 11 digits. You can increase your span slightly by practicing the skill. You can increase it markedly by developing effective encoding strategies (and practicing them). Basically, it comes down to chunking: you need to practice seeing groups of digits as meaningful chunks.

To do this successfully you need some well-learned structure. Some people, for example, have used sports statistics, or addresses and dates. Others have found transforming digits into dollars and cents makes them more meaningful. Others find mathematical relationships memorable (e.g., 632 is memorable if you transform it into 6/3=2).

Word span

How many words you can hold in working memory does depend on (a) how long the words are, and (b) how much they sound the same (you can maintain more dissimilar words). Your word span affects your ability to repeat back unfamiliar words, and therefore is critical to vocabulary acquisition. Your child's quickness in mastering language and your own ability to pick up a foreign language are both partly determined by this aspect of your working memory.

To measure your word span, refer to the appendix at the end of the book.

Reading span

Your ability to repeat back unfamiliar words is critical to your learning of new words, but your ability to understand complex sentences appears to be governed by a separate aspect of working memory. To measure your sentence comprehension, refer to the appendix.

Maximizing your working memory capacity

Working memory capacity is not only about storage—about how *much* information you can hold at one time. After all, it's called *working* memory for a reason—because it contains the information you are working with. The *processing* of information also takes some of your resources. The more resources the processing needs, the less capacity you have available for storage, therefore the less information you can hold. The more skilled you are at processing, the more room you have for information.

In other words, whatever your working memory capacity, you can increase it by practicing appropriate strategies to such a level of mastery that your processing requirements are minimal (the more practiced you are, the less the processing demands).

A larger WM capacity helps you:

⇒ Make better chunks.

⇒ Build more links.

⇒ Abstract themes.

⇒ Integrate new codes with old.

A larger working memory capacity therefore gives you a head start, but the rules are still the same. The important thing is not whether your working memory capacity is high or low, but whether you have mastered appropriate strategies for encoding information. However, if you know your capacity this will help you to decide what strategies are most useful to you.

Putting it together

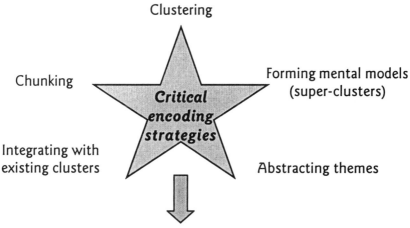

Clustering

Chunking

Forming mental models (super-clusters)

Critical encoding strategies

Integrating with existing clusters

Abstracting themes

Better understanding and recall

Main Ideas

ꙮ Storing memory codes in your permanent database requires information to be transformed from a working memory code to a database code (encoded).

ꙮ Finding memory codes in your database (remembering) requires the database code to be found and transformed into a working memory code (activated).

ꙮ Information may fail to be encoded if too much information is put into working memory at one time.

ꙮ While working memory has a very limited capacity, people do vary in how much they can hold in working memory.

ꙮ Your working memory capacity affects your ability to acquire new information, to understand, to reason and to calculate.

ꙮ You can increase your working memory capacity through practice of various encoding and chunking strategies.

Chapter 7
Review

Memory situation 1

You are having dinner at a restaurant with several friends. The waitress has explained the menu, and answered questions about the ingredients of many of the dishes. You were intending to have seafood, but now, having studied the menu for some minutes, you decide on poultry. But how to decide which dish? You weren't paying attention when the waitress described those items. Now you must ask her to repeat herself.

The principle

You create your memory codes by selecting the information you want.

Memory situation 2

You rush to the post office with your friend's birthday present, slip it into a priority mail envelope, and pause. You left your address book at home. The problem is, your friend has moved several times. You remember two or three different addresses, but which is the current one?

The principle

Memory codes are linked in a network

Memory situation 3

You stop to ask the way. The passer-by tells you, "straight ahead until you get to the lights, turn left, keep going until you get to the gas station on the corner, turn right, then straight ahead, through the traffic circle, and it's the second on the left." You get to the gas station and hesitate. Did they say right or left?

The principle

When you encode or retrieve a code it becomes active (in working memory). If you try to put too much in working memory, you will be unable to encode it all.

Memory situation 4

At the library you are told that you have failed to return a book. You think you have returned it but you can't be sure. You dig out the receipt showing what books you took out at the same time as the missing one, and try to call them to mind. Visualizing the cover of the missing book, you try and recall whether it was with the other books when you returned them. You're still not sure. You remember that the last time you visited the library it had been pouring with rain, and you had been in a hurry to get to the shops before they shut. Now you remember the occasion. And now you clearly remember the cover among the books you placed on the counter.

The principle

To retrieve a code, you follow a trail of cues—codes activating each other along the links between them

Memory situation 5

But unfortunately you are wrong about the cover of the book. Rather than being yellow and gray with a charming watercolor on the front, it was in fact a rather plain blue. You have remembered returning the yellow and gray book, but this is not in fact the missing book.

The principle

Your understanding of your target—your goal—helps you decide what trail to take.

Memory situation 6

You recognize a face in the street, but cannot immediately think who it is. Then you see that they are carrying a bag from Toyworld. A parent, you think. And start to run through the various children-related activities you have been involved with.

The principle

Which trail you choose is influenced by the initial recall cue and your understanding of what it means.

Memory situation 7

You still can't think where you have seen this person before, but then the person goes into an office block. Peering in curiously, you see them standing in the foyer, waiting for an elevator. Of course, that's where you know them from! A previous workplace where you had both worked, many years previously.

The principle

The more similar the encoding and retrieval contexts, the more likely it is that the initial recall cue and retrieval context will send you in the right direction.

Memory situation 8

But perhaps you missed seeing them waiting for an elevator. You have your whole history to choose from. Where on earth do you know this person from? You go through all the places you have lived, the organizations you have been involved with, the places you have worked.

The principle

The less helpful the initial recall cue and context, the more important is your skill at thinking up other possible recall cues.

Memory situation 9

You're in a large restaurant, halfway through your meal. You want to ask your waitress for some water, but realize, staring around the busy room, that you have no idea which is your waitress.

The principle

There is a limit to how helpful retrieval strategies can be—the real key to a good memory lies in encoding.

Memory situation 10

You are at a function at your partner's workplace. Many of the people you've only met once before, at last year's function. You're not even sure which ones work here, and which are partners.

The principle

Links are strong by virtue of having been activated often.

Memory situation 11

But luckily last year you made a special attempt to remember the people that are important to your partner. Because the names of these people were already familiar to you, you had thought of something distinctive about the names before attending the function, and so you could concentrate on selecting something distinctive about the face and linking it with the name.

The principle

To be easily retrieved you need to create a code that is distinctive, and is strongly linked to many other codes.

To remember information that is not "meaningful," meaning must be attached through connection or transformation.

Memory situation 12

Even more impressive to the people you are talking to, you made an effort to memorably encode some personal details about them. For example, one person had spoken of his involvement with his children's school as chairperson of the board of trustees, and various problems the school had been having, such as graffiti being scrawled on the buildings in the weekends, being asked to take a number of children with behavioral problems from other schools, and not being able to find anyone in the school community to take on the job of treasurer. After talking to him you had taken a moment to run through these points, using a few memorable details to enrich the code, and relating them to certain experiences you already had stored (such as the graffiti that once appeared on your own fence). Since you yourself had children at school, the label "BOT" (Board of Trustees) was sufficiently meaningful for use.

When talking to him again, you therefore have a good starting point for conversation, as well as impressing him with your memory!

The principle

Links that are part of a meaningful, tightly integrated cluster are likely to be activated more often (every time any one part of the cluster is activated, each link in the cluster will be activated to some level).

A cluster that is tightly integrated can be labeled by a single, integrated theme.

**Your ability to meaningfully connect
information, to abstract common themes, and
to integrate new information into existing
clusters and networks is affected by your
working memory capacity,
but the most important determinant is your
mastery of the appropriate strategies.**

Effective strategies and their use are discussed in the following chapter.

CHAPTER 8

IDENTIFYING DIFFERENT MEMORY DOMAINS

Memory is not one system, but a set of systems. The different domains of memory have different principles guiding what information they select and how they organize it. To match memory tasks with the appropriate strategies, you need to know what memory domains there are, and how they are different from each other.

Information is not all the same. Different types of information need to be dealt with in different ways. The information contained in a face is treated differently from the information in a textbook. A feeling of grief is remembered in a way that is different from remembering the experience of going to a restaurant.

This seems obvious and yet, when people talk about memory, they tend to speak of it as one thing. Memory is not a "thing." Memory is a process.

The differences between different types of information are not always as obvious as those between events and emotions, faces and facts. For example, here are two similar tasks: (1) you remember you've heard Wynton Marsalis in concert, but you can't immediately remember who accompanied you; (2) you recognize a face as familiar but can't immediately remember who the person is.

The most effective strategy to find the name of the person who accompanied you to the concert is not the same strategy you should use to find the name of the familiar person. The strategies are different because the information you need to identify a person with whom shared an experience relates to the domain of a personal identity, while the information you need to identify a person you are faced with relates to the domain of events.

Differences between information types are significant when they reflect different memory domains.

Knowing the memory domains:

⇒ Helps you distinguish different types of information.

⇒ Helps you distinguish different memory tasks.

⇒ Helps you recognize which strategy is appropriate.

Specific memory domains

Knowledge memory

Knowledge memory contains language and "facts"—information in its narrower, more common meaning. Your knowledge that householders pay money to the local council in return for such services as street lights, sewers, public libraries and parks, etc, is part of knowledge memory. Your knowledge that this money is called "taxes" is also part of knowledge memory. But your knowledge that you pay $159.73 quarterly in taxes is part of personal memory.

Knowledge memory has long been assumed to be organized around concepts—concepts being, as it were, the "theme " of a category. Categories are clusters, or super-clusters. Members of a category belong by virtue of being examples of the theme. The links that connect them is their similarity to each other.

Thus, a domestic cat belongs to the category (cluster) "cat," and to the superordinate category (super-cluster) "mammal." Lions, tigers, leopards, etc, also belong to the category "cat," by virtue of being examples of "catness;" in other words, they share among themselves a certain similarity, based on common features.

Categories are arranged hierarchically, that is, subordinate levels are progressively less abstract:

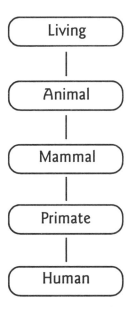

Each of these categories has different information associated with it. Thus, if you are asked whether a spaniel has long ears, you would consult the specific information connected with spaniel, but if you were asked whether a spaniel gives birth to live young, you would find the appropriate information under "Mammal." Of course, accessing information under associated categories takes longer than accessing information within the target category.

If you were asked whether a spaniel lays eggs, it would take you even longer, as properties a category *doesn't* have are rarely explicitly listed. It's also harder to reject an instance as a member of a category when the two items belong to associated categories—for example, it takes you longer to decide that a tree is not an animal (both living) than it does to decide a brick is not an animal.

The fact that knowledge memory is organized in categories explains why category prompts are much more useful than alphabet prompts in retrieval search.

**Use your knowledge about categories to
search more effectively.**

Exercise 8.1

Give yourself 10 seconds to write down all the words you can think
of that start with N. Now give yourself 10 seconds to write down all
the members you can think of that belong to the category "fruit."

Although there are far more words beginning with N than there are
members of the category fruit, nevertheless you probably wrote down
more fruit than words beginning with N.

Differences between experts and novices:

⇛ Experts have *more* categories.

⇛ Experts have *richer* categories.

⇛ Experts' categories are based on deeper principles.

⇛ Novices' categories emphasize surface similarities.

Personal memory

Although Western culture has emphasized the need to improve
knowledge memory, personal memory is at least as important, and
considerably more complex. Personal memory contains several different memory domains. Therefore, many more different strategies
are required to deal with these different domains. Of the 13 common
problem tasks identified in Chapter 1, only two pertain to knowledge
memory.

Personal memory contains at least four domains, two of which
contain several domains of their own.

Memory for yourself

Autobiographical memory is the memory domain concerned
with the information you have about yourself. It includes a domain

that contains information such as whether or not you like ice cream, what your favorite color is, what you think about a political party, etc (*self-description*). This domain is a major part of your sense of identity.

It also includes *emotional memory*. This type of memory can help us control our moods. We can sustain a mood by dwelling on appropriate memories, or change a mood by recalling memories that involve a contrasting emotion.

But people rarely worry about their ability to remember emotions or aspects of their own identity. The domain of interest within autobiographical memory is the domain of events.

There are actually three related domains within *event memory*:

•◆ Memory for specific events that have happened to you.

•◆ Memory for general events, which tells you the broad sequence of actions in events such as going to a restaurant or going to the dentist.

•◆ A summary of your life, which enables you to answer such questions as, "Where did you go to school?" and "Where were you working last year?"

These may be thought of as being connected hierarchically:

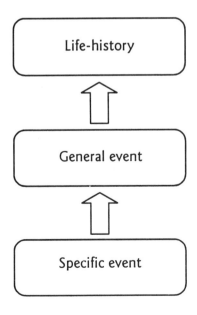

The entry point into the event domain is usually at the general-event level. In other words, if you want to remember the time you went to see *Star Wars*, you would first consider the general event "going to the movies." Because information at this level tends to be accessed relatively often, it is usually very easy to find—so easy in fact that you probably don't even notice doing so.

The memories we have trouble finding are almost always specific events. When did I last go to the movies? Have I read this novel? Where did I go camping two years ago? Who did I go to *Sleepless in Seattle* with?

Because event memory is usually entered via the general-event level, and because the information we are searching for is usually at the specific-event level, it is worth spending a little time explaining the relationship between these two separate domains.

Let us imagine that you have been to the circus only once in your life. If so, you would readily remember that specific occasion. If you had been twice, you would probably remember each occasion, although be uncertain, perhaps, about which occasion some minor detail belonged to. However, if you had been several times to the circus, you would have developed a general *script* for the experience. The separate events would have become merged into this general event, and the specific events would only be remembered if they were marked by something distinctive.

You may have some memory for the first time. You will probably have some memory for the last time. You may remember the time you were very late, or the time a child threw up on your shoes. But by and large the separate events will be lost to you. What you will *not* forget is the general experience of going to the circus—the parts of the event that are usually the same. Maybe the venue, the things on sale, the acts. Maybe a feeling of excitement, a particular smell, a sound, a time of day, a type of weather.

The more often you experience a particular type of event, the stronger your memory for that type of event, but the weaker your memory for the specific occasions. That is why it's so hard to recall the details of your trip to the supermarket two weeks ago.

Moreover, the general script is so powerful that it can lead you into being utterly convinced something happened simply because it fits into the framework of your script.

Memory for events reflects what you *expect* to happen, not simply what *did* happen.

The strength of scripts is perhaps why first experiences tend to be better remembered—on the first occurrence of a new experience, you have no script available and must construct one. Subsequent experiences will be interpreted and encoded in the light of that script.

Similarly, anticipated events are more likely to have some sort of script in place before being actually experienced—hence unexpected events, like novel events, are better remembered.

The more the event breaks with your script for that type of event, the better your memory for that particular event will be. (Failures to remember trivial events, such as where you've put something, or whether you've done something, are reflections of the fact that we pay little attention to routine actions that are, as it were, already scripted.)

To remember an event, select as many distinctive cues as possible.

Your memory for events that have happened to you:
⇒ Includes memory codes for stereotypical features of events and codes summarizing the significant events in your life.
⇒ Is affected by your memory for stereotypical features of events.
⇒ Is clearer and more accurate when there are many distinctive cues.

Are some types of cues more distinctive than others? A Dutch psychologist called Willem Wagenaar kept a detailed diary for six years, recording for each event *who* was involved, *what* the event was, *where* it occurred, and *when* it occurred. At the end of his study he was able to report that the best retrieval cue was *what*, followed by *who* and *where*, and lastly by *when*.

Most of the difference in the power of these details as cues de rives from their relative distinctiveness—*what* is usually the mos distinctive, while *when* is usually the least. The more routine th event, of course, the less distinctive *what* is, and the greater nee you have to find something unusual to mark the event.

It is worth noting what a poor cue *when* is. Unfortunately, we ar time-driven creatures, and we usually are keen to know when some thing happened. Rather than remembering when, we usually hav to work it out, by relating it to other events. It is therefore a goo idea to have a number of *landmark events* readily accessible.

I have found dating events in the past 10 years incomparabl easier because of the advent of children in my life. Children are won derfully useful for providing landmark events. Thus whenever I'm asked when we moved into our current house, I merely recall that we celebrated our son's third birthday in the new house soon afte purchase, and from there (my son's current age being equally acces sible), I can work it out with ease.

The more landmark events you have the easier it is to relate a specific event to the nearest landmark. It is therefore worth your while to establish a number of landmark events at regular intervals.

A landmark event:
⇒ Is readily accessible.
⇒ Occurs on a the date that is memorable or important for you to remember.

Clearly, the more distinctive and memorable events you have in your life, the more landmark events you are likely to have.

Memory for other people

Personal memory also contains *social memory*—that memory for other people and their behavior that enables you to form relation ships and participate in a social group.

Social memory contains the domain that is, more than any other domain, responsible for people's belief that their memory is a problem: *identity memory*. Difficulty in remembering people's names is one of the most common memory tasks that people wish to be better at. And the reason for this is not that their memory is poor, but because it is so embarrassing when their memory lets them down.

We have, in fact, a remarkably good memory for other people's faces. Our memory domain for this particular type of information is not only capacious but also quite complex.

Think about the ease with which you distinguish between hundreds, even thousands, of human faces, and then think about how hard it is to distinguish between the faces of birds, or dogs, or monkeys. This is not because human faces are any more distinctive than the faces of other animals. The differences between human faces are sufficiently subtle that they take a great deal of experience to learn. The importance of learning these subtle differences is shown in the way new babies focus on faces, and prefer them to other objects.

Our memory for other people is, of course, more than a memory for faces, although that part probably has the most impressive capacity. We also remember people's names and various biographical details. We can recognize people by hearing their voice, and at a distance by seeing their shape or the way they move, or even by their clothing. However, faces are the most common and reliable means of identifying a person.

There are three ways we can recognize a person:

- ➥ We might recognize them as having been seen before, without recalling anything about them.

- ➥ We might identify them as a particular person, without recalling their name ("that's my son's friend").

- ➥ We might identify them by name.

If you think about it you will realize that you never, ever, remember a person's name without knowing who she is. This is because names are held in a separate cluster to biographical details, and can only be accessed through the cluster holding those details. You also never recall information about a person without recognizing them as familiar. While this sounds terribly obvious, there is actually a clinical condition whereby a person, while recognizing the people around them, believes they have been replaced by doubles (impostors, robots, aliens, etc). This is simply because the normal accompanying feeling of familiarity is missing.

There are three kinds of identity information that are important for recognizing a person:

- ❧ **Structural codes** (physical features).

- ❧ **Semantic codes** (biographical details, e.g., occupation, marital status, address).

- ❧ **Name codes.**

There is a fourth type of code that is useful for remembering unfamiliar faces:

- ❧ **Visually-derived semantic codes** (e.g., age, gender, attributions such as "he looks honest/intelligent/sly").

Semantic codes that are visually derived have an advantage over *biographical codes*, because the link with the structural code is meaningful and thus strong, whereas the connection between the structural codes and biographical details is entirely arbitrary. To say someone looks like a fox connects meaningfully with the person's facial features, whereas to say that someone is a lawyer has no particular connection with the person's face (to say someone *looks* like a lawyer would of course be meaningfully connected).

> **Visually-derived semantic codes are useful**
> **for remembering new faces because**
> **the link with the physical features of the face**
> **is strong and meaningful.**

However you cannot *identify* a person without reference to the biographical codes.

The interesting aspect of these different codes is that you can only access them in a particular order:

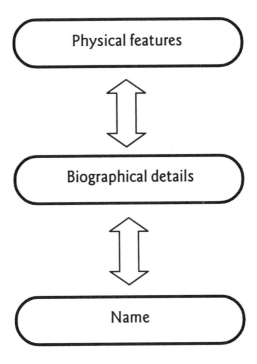

When you recognize a face as familiar but can't recall anything about the person, the structural code has failed to trigger the biographical code. When you identify a person by recalling details about them, but cannot recall their name, the biographical code has failed to trigger the name code.

From the list of 13 memory tasks that people most commonly are concerned about, four relate to identity memory:

•◆ Trying to put a name to a face.

•◆ Trying to put a face to a name.

•◆ Trying to remember who someone is (e.g. "local librarian").

•◆ Meeting someone and wanting to remember details such as names of children and partner, any problems they may have been having last time you talked, etc.

We can now interpret these problems as:

1. Trying to put a name to a face.   Accessing name code from structural code.

2. Trying to put a face to a name.   Accessing structural code from name code.

3. Trying to remember who someone is.   Accessing biographical code from structural code.

4. Trying to remember personal details.   Accessing event information from structural code.

From our diagram it is evident why the third of these problems is the easiest. Accessing a name code from the structural code requires you first to access the biographical code. Whether the name code is then triggered depends on the strength of the link between them.

You will have noticed that in the last problem I suggested that event information was required, rather than the biographical code. Details such as what you talked about last time you met will be encoded in the event domain. Some details may be encoded in the knowledge domain (for example, the films a particular actor has appeared in). When you remember some details about a person but not others, it is likely that those details are encoded in a separate domain, and have not automatically activated with the biographical code.

In the main then, memory failures on these common identity tasks are due to weak links between the different codes. Therefore, to improve your memory for identity information, you should concentrate on strategies that strengthen the links between (a) the structural codes and the biographical codes, and (b) the biographical codes and the name code.

However, there is another weak point, and that is the structural codes themselves. As I have said, the differences between faces are subtle. Constructing an accessible structural code requires you to select features for encoding that will enable you to readily distinguish that particular face from others. Some faces, it must be said, make this very difficult.

In general, Caucasians tend to pay more attention to the upper half of the face—to the hair and eyes. Of course, this is not true of races whose hair and eyes tend to be much more similar. The mouth is also closely attended to, but, as with eyes, this is chiefly because the mouth and eyes are very informative as to a person's emotions. Although we attend to these features while in conversation with a person, we do not necessarily remember that information beyond that time. Interestingly the chin, then the cheeks, then lines, all seem to be attended to more than the nose (although the nose is often cited as a distinctive feature).

However, notwithstanding these generalizations, different people do focus on different facial features. When I was a child, I categorized people by the shape of their face. There is no rule which specifies that one particular feature is more distinctive than another. What's important is what works for you.

What is important to note is that familiar faces tend to be encoded differently from new faces, and the difference suggests how we can more rapidly make a face familiar. Structural codes for familiar faces emphasize the more informative and less changeable features—for example, although initially we pay most attention to hair, hair is probably the most changeable feature we possess. The more familiar a person is, the less we are thrown by changes in hairstyle or hair color. But we can completely fail to recognize someone we don't know well when they change their hair.

**To encode a new face effectively, focus on
features that can't be changed.**

To improve your memory for other people, you should:
⇒ Strengthen the link between the name code and the biographical code.
⇒ Strengthen the link between the biographical code and related codes in other domains.
⇒ Concentrate on less changeable aspects when encoding the facial features.

Remembering how to do things

Skill memory is quite different from all the other kinds of information that have been discussed so far. This difference is often described as the distinction between knowing *how* and knowing *that*.

It is generally agreed that practical knowledge must be organized quite differently than factual knowledge.

Initially, a skill is learned through verbal instruction, but this necessary first step is then succeeded by an *associative stage*, during which you coordinate the physical actions and strengthen the connections between successive actions. During this stage you still need the verbal reminders to tell you what to do, however, in the third and final stage you lose the verbalization entirely. By this stage, through practice of the action sequence, you have achieved autonomy—the skill becomes automatic, no thought is needed, and indeed thinking (verbalizing) only serves to hinder your performance. A skill is not properly mastered until it becomes automatic.

For example, many of us have had the experience of trying to teach someone to drive a car. How often did you have to close your eyes and imagine yourself going through the motions before you could actually explain the sequence of movements needed? A skill is not truly acquired until you can "do it without thinking." Having to think what comes next only impedes the flow of actions.

Interestingly (and probably against common sense), there appears to be no mental limit to the *autonomous stage*. Of course your physical condition sets a limit to how much improvement you can make to a practical skill, but a cognitive skill will continue to improve as long as you keep practicing. One long-ago researcher had two people perform 10,000 mental addition problems, and they kept on increasing their speed to the end.

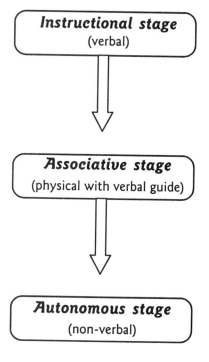

Instructional stage
(verbal)

Associative stage
(physical with verbal guide)

Autonomous stage
(non-verbal)

Practice is the key to mastering a skill. One of the critical aspects is assuredly the fact that, with practice, the demands on your attention get smaller and smaller.

While practice is the key, there are some actions we can take to ensure we get the most value out of our practice:

- ◆◆ Specific examples rather than abstract rules seem to be more important. Rules are eventually abstracted from examples, but examples continue to be important because they are more accessible.

- ◆◆ Feedback is very important. However, to be beneficial it needs to occur while the action is active in memory. The next attempt also needs to occur while the feedback is active in memory.

- ◆◆ Skills learned under variable circumstances generalize better to new situations than skills learned under rigid or specific circumstances. It's better to practice a skill with subtle variations (such as varying the force of your pitch, or the distance you are throwing) rather than trying to repeat your action exactly.

- ◆◆ Spacing your practice is probably even more important for skill learning than for learning factual information (math textbooks, for example, tend to put similar exercises together, but in fact they would be better spaced out).

- ◆◆ If skills share components with already mastered skills, learning will be easier (e.g., learning a tennis volley is easier if you have learned a badminton volley).

- ◆◆ If a new skill contains steps that are antagonistic to steps contained in an already mastered skill, that new skill will be much harder to learn (e.g., when I changed keyboards, the buttons for page up, page down, insert, etc, had been put in a different order—the conflict between the old habit and the new pattern made learning the new pattern more difficult). The existing skill may also be badly affected.

- ◆◆ Whether or not it is better to try and learn a skill whole, or break it down into components and learn them separately, depends on whether the parts are independent (e.g., computer programming can be broken into independent sub-skills, but learning to play the piano is best learned as a whole).

To master a skill:

⇒ Practice it until you reach the stage where actions follow automatically.

⇒ Practice more efficiently, by:

   1. Varying your actions.

   2. Providing immediate feedback.

   3. Spacing out your practice.

Remembering to do things

Planning memory is sometimes termed future memory—a pleasantly paradoxical name. It contains your plans and goals (such as, "I must pick up the dry cleaning today" and "I intend to finish this project within three months"). As with forgetting someone's name, forgetting to do something comes high on the list of memory tasks people would like to be better at. And the reason is the same—forgetting to do something can often cause you much embarrassment.

Our intentions—the information in the planning domain—appear to be organized around goals. We remember goal-directed activities much more easily than other activities, and we remember the actual achievement of these goals best of all.

But remembering intentions is much more difficult than remembering events that have happened, and the primary reason is the lack of retrieval cues. This is why, of all memory tasks, remembering to do things relies most heavily on memory aids outside our own minds. Reminder notes, calendars, diaries, watch alarms, oven timers, leaving objects in conspicuous places—all these external aids act as retrieval cues.

In general, when we form an intention, we link it either to an event ("after we go to the pool, we'll go to the supermarket") or a time ("at 2 p.m. I must call Fred"). When, as so often, these *trigger events* or times fail to remind us of our intention, it is because the link between the trigger and the intention is not strong enough.

Partly this is because the trigger is not in itself particularly distinctive. Your failure to remember to call Fred at 2 p.m., for example, may be because you paid little attention to the clock reaching that time, or because there were other competing activities triggered by that same time signal.

Although planning memory has the disadvantage of poor and few retrieval cues, it does appear to compensate for this somewhat by being more easily triggered by quite marginal cues. Thus a friend of mine was reminded that her son's friend would be spending Saturday night with them when she saw an advertisement for a movie about John F. Kennedy (the child's father had the same initials: JFK).

Not all planning is linked to a trigger event or time. Quite a lot of planning simply waits upon an appropriate opportunity ("must buy some stamps sometime"). Such intentions usually need quite explicit cues. Thus, if I happened to see stamps on sale, I would probably remember my intention, but walking past, or even into, a shop that happens to sell stamps may not be enough to trigger my memory.

On the other hand, I might keep being reminded of my intention when I am in the same context as when I originally encoded the intention (when I am not in a position to carry it out!). Hence our increasing exasperation that we can never remember a particular intention when we are able do something about it.

To deal with opportunistic planning, you should try to specify features of an appropriate opportunity when encoding the intention. Thus, to remember to buy bread on the way home, you should think about what actions you need to take to buy the bread (for example, going a different route) and try to form a strong link between the trigger event and your action ("Today when I get to the traffic lights I'll turn *left*").

A reminder of your intention is much less effective than being reminded of both the trigger event and the intended activity. Even being reminded of the trigger event is better than being reminded of the intention on its own.

**To remind yourself to do something, focus on
the trigger, not the intent itself.**

Don't assume that because something is important to you, you will automatically remember it. Somewhat to their surprise, researchers have found no evidence that personal importance has any effect on the likelihood of remembering to do something.

Common problem memory tasks, grouped by domain:

Knowledge memory:

- ⚭ Remembering information you have studied.

- ⚭ Remembering words.

Identity memory:

- ⚭ Trying to put a name to a face.

- ⚭ Trying to put a face to a name.

- ⚭ Trying to remember who someone is.

- ⚭ Wanting to remember someone's personal details.

Event memory:

- ⚭ Remembering whether you've done something.

- ⚭ Remembering where you've put something.

- ⚭ Remembering when/where something happened.

- ⚭ Remembering important dates.

Planning memory:

- ⚭ Remembering to do something at a particular time.

- ⚭ Knowing there's something you need to remember but you can't think what it is.

Skill memory:

- ⚭ Trying to remember how to do something.

Although there are many different types of information, most of our memory problems concern only five types of information:

1. Remembering facts.	–Knowledge memory.
2. Remembering people.	–Identity memory.
3. Remembering events.	–Event memory.
4. Remembering to do something.	–Planning memory.
5. Remembering procedures.	–Skill memory

Putting it together

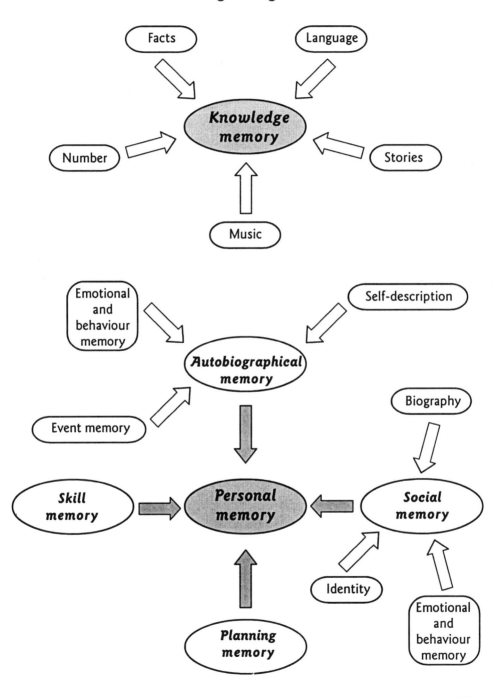

Main Ideas

∽ To classify different memory tasks and different types of information, you need to know what types of memory domain there are.

∽ There are three different types of memory code for events: general codes for stereotypical features of events; summary codes for the fact of significant events; the codes for the specific event itself.

∽ Your memory for other people is also distributed among several different types of memory code. Difficulties in remembering people's names or details about them is due to weak links between the appropriate memory codes.

∽ To learn a skill you need to practice it until you reach the stage where actions follow automatically.

∽ To remember to do something you should link the intended activity with a trigger. To the extent that the trigger is well-chosen and the link between trigger and intention is strong, your recall will be improved.

CHAPTER 9
STUDY STRATEGIES

Elaborations are effective to the extent that they reduce the arbitrariness of information to be learned. Successful learners create elaborations that enhance the significance of the information. Much of this elaboration is achieved by asking relevant questions. The strategy of asking questions and evaluating their relevance is central to most formal study skill programs.

A classification of memory strategies

Our aim is to match memory strategies with the appropriate memory tasks. But there are a great many memory strategies. We need some means of reducing the number of strategies to be considered for any particular task. We need a classification system.

Memory strategies range from the very specific (*Every Good Boy Deserves Fruit*, for learning the notes on the treble staff) to the very general (monitoring your learning). In general, the more specific strategies are those that manipulate the information you wish to remember, while the more general strategies are those that help you learn more effectively (*support strategies*).

I have emphasized the distinction between information that needs to be memorized verbatim and information that needs to be understood and remembered for meaning. These different goals require different strategies. In this chapter we will look at information-manipulation strategies for meaningful information.

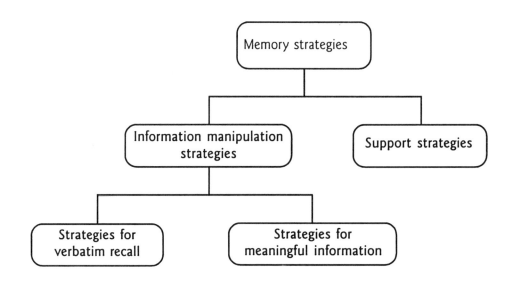

Manipulating information for understanding and recall

I will use the term *study strategies* as a convenient shorthand for encoding strategies that are aimed at helping your understanding and recall of meaningful information.

To encode meaningful information for better recall we must understand it, and we must understand it sufficiently well that we can select the information that needs to be given special attention. *USA—Understand, Select, Attend*—these are the processes underlying our study strategies.

The effective use of any study strategy hinges on your ability to select and attend to the important information. Your evaluation of any specific strategy is based on this fundamental principle.

Study strategies are valuable to the extent that they help you understand the information and distinguish the important information from the less important.

The two main study strategies are *active reading* and *taking notes*. Both of these are general strategies containing a number of more specific strategies.

Taking notes

The sort of information for which we use a note-taking strategy (information from books; information from a formal spoken presentation) comes to us already packaged. Someone has produced the material, and the same specific note-taking strategies have probably been used, to a greater or lesser extent, by the writer or speaker to help you understand and remember the information.

Note-taking has two aspects:

➽ A *strategy* that you can use to render information more comprehensible and memorable.

➽ A *cue* to the level of difficulty of the material and its organization.

Most people probably believe that they are taking notes to provide a written record of information they need to remember. But research reveals that the primary value of note-taking is through its effect on how you encode the information.

For this reason, note-taking is effective to the extent that you paraphrase, organize and make sense of the information while taking notes. Notes that are simply taken down verbatim, without thought, are not likely to be effective (unless you later rewrite and reorganize them).

Conditions for effective note-taking:

⇒ Slow or self-determined rate of presentation.

⇒ Well-organized material.

⇒ Material that is not too difficult or complicated.

⇒ Skill at note-taking.

Note-taking is a strategy for making information meaningful.

With this in mind, let's take a look at the component strategies of note-taking.

Highlighting

Highlighting refers to any means of emphasizing key words or phrases, such as underlining, framing, using bold type, using a colored marker, etc.

Highlighting as a cue:

⇒ Cues you to the details the author regarded as important.

⇒ Is effective in helping you remember highlighted details—but at the expense of other information.

⇒ Is therefore effective only if the author's goals match your own.

Highlighting as a strategy:

⇒ Focuses your attention.

⇒ Encourages you to spend more time on the material.

⇒ Therefore improves your recall of both the highlighted details *and* the rest of the text.

Conditions for effective highlighting:

⇒ Sufficient time.

⇒ Material that is not too dense (too many important ideas).

⇒ Material that is not too difficult (ideas too complex to convey by key words or phrase).

⇒ Use of only one or two different types of cue.

⇒ Use only one highlighted phrase per paragraph.

⇒ Skill in selecting key concepts.

Headings

A story has a very clear and strong shape, something we all begin to understand and use from a young age. In stories, the narrative is held together by a *causal chain*—a string of causal connections from the protagonist's goal to the outcome. To the extent that this chain is clear, the story will be easy to remember.

Explanatory text however tends to be more disconnected than the average story (and hence more difficult to remember, for your recall depends heavily on how well-connected the information is). Accordingly a number of strategies have been devised for emphasizing changes of topic and the organizational structure of the text. One such strategy is the use of *headings*.

Headings as a cue
⇒ Are valuable to the extent that they link changes of topic.

⇒ Can act as labels for clusters.

⇒ Must therefore be used as retrieval cues to be useful.

⇒ Can help you produce better summaries.

⇒ Are little needed if the text has few changes of topic.

To assess whether headings used in a text are of value to you, ask yourself the following questions:

•• Do they highlight the main points and themes?

•• Do they provide meaningful connections between topics?

•• Do they provide good retrieval cues?

Headings as a strategy
You might restructure the text using your own headings:

⇒ Where text is not organized in this fashion.

⇒ Where it is poorly done.

⇒ Where the author's goals and interests are not the same as yours.

⇒ As a strategy to abstract section themes.

Exercise 9.1

Go through chapter 6 and note down the headings and subheadings. Now look at each section and write down what you think is its main point under each section heading.

Do the headings bear on the main points?

Are the headings short enough, or contain a key word or phrase, that would be a useful retrieval cue?

Can you think of better ones?

Summaries

Summaries summarize the main points without adding any new information or offering a new perspective. They may be a straightforward string of factual statements (*topical summaries*) or they may reorganize text into a different format (*graphic summaries*)—for example, in the form of *outlines, graphic organizers, multimedia summaries* or *maps*.

The list of "Main Ideas" at the end of each chapter in the book is an example of a topical summary.

To summarize effectively it is critical that you re-state the main ideas and themes in your own words. It is a poor strategy to copy out the sentences that look important and ignore the rest. If there was no value in those intervening sentences, the author wouldn't have bothered writing them! A good summary sentence condenses the important information in a paragraph into a new statement. It is a good idea therefore to try and produce summaries without looking at the text. The extent to which summarizing is an effective strategy depends on your skill at distinguishing important information from less important.

Outlines and graphic organizers are useful strategies for hierarchical information. Compare the following two examples (taken from Robinson and Kiewra, 1995). The first is an outline and the second is a graphic organizer.

Schizophrenia

I. Simple
    A. % of Americans   1/10
    B. Symptoms: Gradual withdrawal and disinterest in the world
    C. Severity: Most likely to fend for themselves

II. Paranoid
    A. % of Americans   1
    B. Symptoms: Feeling of being persecuted
    C. Severity: May live in a marginal way

III. Catatonic
    A. % of Americans   1/10
    B. Symptoms: Peculiar motor behavior alternating between stupor and frenzy
    C. Severity: Series of short attacks over many years

IV. Hebephrenic
    A. % of Americans   3/4
    B. Symptoms: Regressive behavior and total disregard for personal hygiene
    C. Severity: Most severe

Schizophrenia

	Simple	Paranoid	Catatonic	Hebephrenic
% of Americans	1/10	1	1/10	3/4
Symptoms	Gradual withdrawal and disinterest in the world	Feeling of being persecuted	Peculiar motor behaviour alternating between stupor and frenzy	Regressive behaviour and total disregard for personal hygiene
Severity	Most likely to fend for themselves	May live in a marginal way	Series of short attacks over many years	Most severe

Outlines are easier to produce than graphic organizers—hence their popularity—but in general they are less effective. In the outline, the clusters *within* a concept are clear, but the relations *between* concepts—between the clusters—are not. A graphic organizer allows connections between clusters to be more readily seen.

Graphic organizers:
⇒ Need more time to process than outlines.

⇒ Are of little value when the text is short and simple.

⇒ Are helpful for constructing super-clusters.

Outlines:
⇒ Are easier and quicker to process than graphic organizers.

⇒ Are effective for rote-learning facts.

Multimedia summaries are particularly appropriate (and valuable) for scientific explanations. In multimedia summaries pictures and words are combined.

Rules for effective multimedia summaries:
⇒ Be very concise.

⇒ Use a minimum of text.

⇒ Coordinate words and images

Probably the most widely useful type of summary is a **map**. Although several different mapping strategies have been developed (**mind-mapping** is of course the most famous), the basic idea is the same for them all: information is organized into a "map" that graphically displays the main points and clusters them into useful groupings. The essential characteristic is that information is *not* displayed in a linear or hierarchical fashion. A map begins in the center of a page, and moves out in all directions.

Here is a partially completed map of chapter 6:

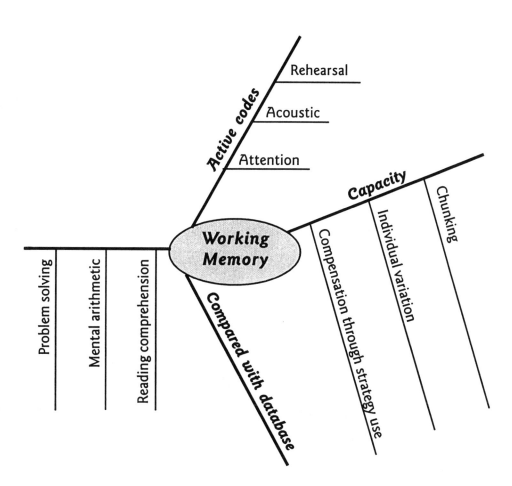

Basic mapping technique:
⇒ Select a key word with several lines extended out from it.
⇒ Skim the text to select secondary headings.
⇒ Write these headings on the lines radiating from the key word.
⇒ Recall details without looking at the text and add them to the map.
⇒ Reread the text and add further details.

The essence of a map is that it provides a retrieval structure. Producing the map helps you organize the information, and once produced, provides a summary for later review. The map also emphasizes new vocabulary—a large part of science learning concerns the learning of technical terms.

A crucial step in the strategy is the attempt to recall details without looking at the text. By making yourself dredge for the information, you will be forcing yourself to dig out related information from your existing store of knowledge.

Exercise 9.2
See how many more details you can add to the map of chapter 6 without referring to the text, then check back and add more.

Making note-taking an effective strategy
Several factors affect whether or not note-taking is effective:

•• How fast the information is presented (note-taking is more likely to aid recall if presentation rate is slow and you can review your notes.)

•• The density/complexity of the information.

- The style of the presentation (for example, a very formal, "dry" text is more likely to be recorded verbatim, while a more informal passage is more likely to be paraphrased).

- How well the information is organized.

- How skilled you are at taking notes (in particular, your skill at capturing the most important points).

Rules for effective note-taking:

⇒ **Select.** Omit trivial and redundant details. Omit anything you'll recall anyway!

⇒ **Condense.** Replace lists with a category term.

⇒ **Organize.** Choose headings and topic sentences.

⇒ **Rephrase.** Use your own words.

Note in particular the instruction to omit anything you'll remember anyway. This is trickier than it might sound. We feel that, of course, we must note down the most important facts, but often the most important facts are the ones we'll remember anyway. The information we really need to record is the middle tier information—the information that is not *the* most important, but is important. Note-taking is usually performed in a situation where time is limited. Time taken to record information that you'll remember without noting it is time taken from noting down less memorable information.

Your selection of important information is affected by:

⇒ The structure of the text.

⇒ The density of the text.

⇒ Cues in the text.

⇒ Any instructions or objectives stated at the beginning of the text.

⇒ Personal interest and relevance.

Active reading

The key to taking notes effectively is in the wise selection of information. Remember *USA*—before we can select, we must understand. And to understand we must read effectively.

Reading is in itself quite a passive process. Successful students tend to read actively, that is, they think about the information they are reading, ask themselves questions about it, and try to relate it to information they already have. Poor students on the other hand, tend to simply read, and their primary strategy to help their understanding and memory of the material is simply to reread it.

There are a number of active reading strategies.

One well-known, but frequently misunderstood, active reading strategy is *skimming*. Many people believe this is actually a poor strategy, which is hardly surprising when you realize that skimming has been variously described as: reading only the first and last words of a sentence; reading very rapidly; missing the long words. In fact, if done well, skimming is a very effective strategy, for it is all about actively searching text for critical information.

Reading is a complex skill that takes place at a number of levels. In the first place, the physical features of the letters must be recognized and interpreted. Then the words, the meaningful chunks of phrases, the idea stated in a sentence. Many readers go no further than this, but an effective reader goes beyond, to the level of main ideas, and of themes. But a reader who attends only to the "higher" levels—to the main ideas and themes—risks missing significant details. Attention must be paid to each level of the decoding process. For most of us, the first levels—the decoding of letters and words— is such a practiced skill that we need to expend little resources on them. Decoding at higher levels may require considerably more

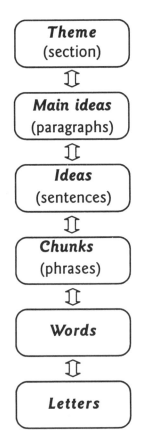

Theme (section)

⇕

Main ideas (paragraphs)

⇕

Ideas (sentences)

⇕

Chunks (phrases)

⇕

Words

⇕

Letters

attention. Bearing in mind the limited capacity of working memory, you should accordingly focus on only one level at one time. Thus, if the material is particularly complex, you would attack it first chunk by chunk, then at the sentence-level (ideas), then at paragraph-level (main ideas), before trying to grasp the theme at section-level.

Active reading strategies include the following:

Search strategies:

- ➡ Jumping forward or backward in the text to find particular information.

- ➡ Skimming through the text for particular information.

- ➡ Anticipating information that might be covered in the text, and hunting for it.

Clarifying strategies:

- ➡ Backtracking for clarification.

- ➡ Attending to figures and tables.

- ➡ Re-stating text in own words.

Elaborating strategies:

- ➡ Moving back and forth between different parts (perhaps between a table and the text) to integrate them.

- ➡ Thinking of analogies or examples.

- ➡ Drawing conclusions.

Evaluating strategies:

- ➡ Evaluating the difficulty of the text, and how well you are understanding it.

- ➡ Noting whether information is previously known.

- ➡ Evaluating the relevance of the information to your own goals.

- ➡ Evaluating the quality of the information.

As specific note-taking strategies must be evaluated in terms of their usefulness in helping you select the most important information, so active reading strategies must be evaluated in terms of their usefulness in helping you understand the information.

Note-taking is about selection.

Active reading is about understanding.

A key component of any search for understanding requires that you link the information being presented with related information that you have in your database. Such connections are achieved through *elaboration*.

Elaboration strategies

Elaboration means going beyond the information presented.

Elaborative strategies were developed in the context of learning pairs of associated items, as when you learn that *aronga* means *direction* in Maori. The elaboration in this context could involve joining the two items into a common phrase or image (e.g., "you're going in the *wrong direction*")—thus forming a link between them.

While language learning (foreign languages; new vocabulary in your native language; technical jargon) is all about linking pairs of words, such learning is of little direct practical relevance to most classes of information that we want to remember. But the basic concept of elaboration is easily extended to more complex material.

Consider the following text, imagining that you wish to learn the biographical facts about this (fictitious) person (the example is taken from a 1987 study by McCormick and Levin):

> Born and raised on a dairy *farm* where she helped take care of the cows, *Charlene McKune* has always been used to hard work. When she was a child, McKune enjoyed creating homes for her pets out of her toy *building blocks*. To earn extra money and because of her hatred for dirt of any kind, McKune began *washing cars* for her parents" friends.

The italicized words highlight the critical information.

One method of elaborating this information to make it more memorable would be to transform it into an interactive image (*transformational elaboration*—this strategy is discussed in the next chapter). By coding the proper name (*Charlotte McKune*) as an imageable similar-sounding word (*raccoon*), the highlighted information can be transformed into a mental picture of a pet *raccoon* outside a *farm*house jumping over a long row of *building blocks* with some children *washing cars* nearby.

A second strategy (*non-transformational elaboration*) involves abstracting a unifying theme and rewriting the information as an integrated cluster around this theme:

> *Charlene McKune* spent much of her life living in the serenity of the remote countryside. Born and raised on a *farm*, McKune grew to love the peace and quiet of rural living. When she was a child, her father made her *building blocks* out of bits of wood on the farm, and McKune spent hours building "barns" and "silos" with these blocks. To earn extra money, McKune began *washing cars*—and sometimes tractors—for the neighboring farmers.

Transformational vs. non-transformational elaborative strategies:

⇒ Transformational strategies introduce relationships into the to-be-learned material that are not always naturally connected.

⇒ Transformational strategies can aid memory, but because the relationships are arbitrary, they do not help you understand the material.

⇒ Non-transformational strategies add information that is naturally and meaningfully connected.

⇒ Non-transformational strategies, because they enrich the information to be learned with a greater number of meaningful connections, aid understanding, as well as memory.

Exercise 9.3

Can you abstract the unifying theme of the second passage about Charlene McKune?

If the critical information to learn had been *cows, hard work, pets, hating dirt*, what might the theme be?

Can you re-write the passage to reflect this theme?

———————

Elaborative interrogation

Elaborative interrogation is a non-transformational elaborative strategy. The idea behind the strategy is that relevant prior knowledge is not always readily activated when you are trying to learn new information, and sometimes help is needed to make the right connections. The strategy requires you to go beyond the information given to you and to construct reasons for the relationships between bits of information.

For example, consider the following passage (taken from a 1990 study by Woloshyn, Willoughby, Wood, and Pressley):

> The park-like atmosphere at the University of Calgary is partially maintained by the school's policy that no cars be allowed on campus. Some of Canada's best research institutes, like the Arctic Institute of North America, are located on or near the campus. The university also has a wilderness information and communication center on campus. The school has a theater that is modeled on Stratford. The school's art museum has a very fine collection of ancient coins. Unfortunately, the school offers very few intramural sports.

The elaborative interrogation strategy involves turning the facts to be learned into why-questions (e.g., Why are some of the country's best research institutes located on or near this campus?), and then answering them.

The strategy is of proven effectiveness when the information to be learned concerns familiar concepts. Remember, elaborative techniques help your understanding by relating new information to codes already stored and familiar to you. Thus elaborative interrogation is a strategy best suited to a situation where the information you wish to learn relates to a rich network of information in your database.

**Elaborative interrogation is effective
to the extent that it forces you to construct
a better super-cluster.**

However, if the underlying concepts themselves are new, elaborative interrogation is of little use (except perhaps to indicate to you the holes in your knowledge!).

Elaborative interrogation is useful:
⇒ When you require comprehension as well as recall.
⇒ Only when you already possess sufficient related knowledge.

Elaboration to add meaning

As we know, to be memorable, information needs to have strong links with accessible codes (potential retrieval cues). Links gain strength from each other, and the best way of encoding information is as a cluster tightly integrated through the sharing of a common theme.

Elaboration is about connecting new information with old. It is about adding meaning.

For example, consider the following facts:

Arteries are thick and elastic and carry blood rich in oxygen from the heart.

Veins are thinner and less elastic and carry blood rich in carbon dioxide back to the heart.

Now, assuming that you know little about anatomy and this information is quite new to you, there are basically three ways you can approach learning this information. The simplest and least effective is to simply rehearse it *ad nauseam* until firmly entrenched through brute force. A more effective approach would be to use a mnemonic strategy (see next chapter), which makes arbitrary information more memorable. Thus, for example, you could create memorable sentences such as "*Art*(ery) was *thick* around the middle so he wore pants with an *elastic* waistband."

However, although this would be helpful if these facts are all the anatomy you wish to acquire, such mnemonics don't help you master anatomy. To develop understanding, you must use a different approach—non-transformational elaboration: building superclusters.

The critical feature, it is argued, is that you understand the *significance* of the information. Being provided with a raft of additional facts which relate to the information to be learned does not necessarily help, and may indeed hinder memory if the facts are not directly relevant.

Thus, in our present example, you would ask yourself, why are arteries thicker and more elastic than veins? Does it relate to their different functions? Perhaps arteries need to be elastic because blood is pumped out of the heart in spurts, whereas veins, carrying the blood back to the heart, have less need to be able to expand or contract. (The example is taken from a study by Bransford, Stein, Shelton, and Owings.)

Elaborations are effective to the extent that they reduce the arbitrariness of the links between codes.

Experts in a field make such elaborations readily. It may well be that this skill is critical in distinguishing successful learners from poor learners.

The poorer your skill at generating effective elaborations, the more you need information to be presented to you with such elaborations spelled out. If you are skilled at seeking out meaningful relationships between facts you will be less affected by the quality of the material presented to you.

Elaborative strategies do require a greater working memory capacity than a simple strategy such as rehearsal. However, the capacity demands of complex strategies become less as you become more skilled at them.

Elaborating to develop expertise.

⇒ Elaboration is effective to the extent that it meaningfully connects information.

⇒ Elaboration is effective to the extent that it explains the relationships between facts.

⇒ Elaboration is effective to the extent that it increases the number of retrieval paths.

⇒ Asking questions is an effective way to go beyond the information presented to you.

⇒ Asking "why" questions is an effective means of producing meaningful and relevant associations.

Exercise 9.4:
Testing your understanding of effective elaborations.

(a) Which is more memorable: "the donkey *and* the hedge;" "the donkey *by* the hedge;" or "the donkey *in* the hedge"?

(b) Which list is more memorable?

Shell—well	Ponce—purse	money—purse
car—star	Money—nanny	sand—shell
mouse—house	dress—brass	car—mat
bat—mat	soil– soul	brass—star

Applying the right study strategy

To decide on the most effective study strategies in a situation where you have meaningful information to understand and remember, you need to first evaluate the information.

We can classify text at one of three different levels, according to its structure and density:

1. Simple (straightforward text with clear connections).

2. Complex (characterized by many changes of topic and more than one level of information).

3. Difficult (dense text with many topic changes, often unclear, inconsistent and/or abstract).

These different types of text require progressively more complex strategies.

Within each level there are gradations of complexity/difficulty, and these also affect your choice of strategy and the number of different strategies you require.

To assess the difficulty of text:

⇒ Assess density:
How many different ideas are there in each paragraph? How many on a page?

⇒ Assess the effectiveness of the structure:
Is it divided into logical sections? Do the headings encapsulate the themes of the sections? Are changes of theme signaled by headings?

⇒ Look for the presence of effective cues:
Are key points highlighted?

⇒ Assess complexity:
Can important concepts be easily conveyed in single words or brief phrases? Is the information in each section meaningfully connected? How many changes of theme (topic) are there?

⇒ Compare style:
Does the approach match your own?

We can classify study strategies into six broad processes:

Broad processes	**Specific strategies**
Re-stating	Paraphrasing; visualizing; transformational elaboration
Selecting	Underlining, highlighting, boxes, lists
Abstracting themes	Headings, summaries
Perceiving structure	Outlines, graphic organizers
Making sense of information	Elaborative interrogation, analogies, maps, multimedia summaries, re-structuring, charts and tables, integrating sections of text
Monitoring comprehension	Constructing and testing theories about the meaning of the text, seeking additional information

We can now match these processes against our classes of text (where the processes beside the text levels indicate the *additional* processes required):

Simple text	Re-statement
Complex text	Selecting
	Abstracting themes
	Perceiving structure
	Making sense of information
Difficult text	Monitoring Comprehension

Remember, when you evaluate any specific study strategy the critical questions are:

Does it help you understand the information?

Does it help you select the important information?

This is a question not simply about the value of a specific strategy in a particular context, but also a question about *you*. We are all slightly different in the way we approach and perceive information. What works for me won't necessarily work for you. When you choose a strategy, you must also consider your own *learning style*.

Your personal learning style

The deep versus the surface approach

A number of different learning styles have been identified by various researchers and writers, but perhaps the most fundamental difference is that between a *deep approach* to learning and a *surface approach*. A deep approach seeks meaning, while a surface approach aims simply to be able to reproduce information.

A further distinction can be made depending on whether you direct your attention to the global features of experiences, or prefer a point-by-point analysis of details (and especially enjoy the specification of rules).

	Deep	**Surface**
Global	Search for meaning by organizing the material into an integrated whole.	Memorize a ready-made organized whole.
Analytic	Search for meaning by analyzing isolated items.	Memorize isolated items.

Of course, these distinctions are not exclusive of each other. We all use each one of these approaches at different times and in different situations. Personal interest, the skills and enthusiasm of a particular teacher, and particular subjects all influence our approach to a learning task.

Physical sciences, for example, tend to emphasize detail, and a deep approach may superficially be very similar to a surface approach. However, although sciences need a more analytic approach, you must be careful that you don't get bogged down in too much detail. Understanding cause-and-effect relations are important, and require a search for meaning.

In general, in any subject, a deep approach is a far superior approach if you are intending to acquire a certain level of expertise.

The most effective approach, if your goal is understanding as well as remembering, is searching for the underlying, connecting principles. Even vocabulary can be understood rather than simply memorized. Few words are arbitrary. If you understand the derivations of words, you are much more likely to remember them.

If your goal is, however, simply to pass exams, then rote-learning is perfectly adequate for regurgitating facts (as long as you aren't going to be asked questions that require you to go beyond the information you have been given and demonstrate that you can draw the right inferences from the underlying concepts and principles you have ostensibly learned). The key, as always, is in your selection of the "right" information to be memorized.

Students who follow a surface approach are usually mainly concerned with achieving a task and fulfilling its requirements. Such students typically are happy for the teachers to set the learning tasks, and are primarily interested in the qualification they will achieve. Students who are interested in the subject for itself, on the other hand, are more likely to want to play a part in setting their own learning boundaries, and tend to actively dislike examinations and lectures (which reflect the teacher's boundaries). Students who take a deep approach usually do much better than students who take a surface approach.

Transcending your personal style

Both global and analytic approaches have their advantages—a truly flexible strategist has a style that integrates both approaches. What is critical is not so much what your style is, but its suitability for the style of presentation of the information you have to learn. You learn better when the task matches your style. You need to spend more time on information presented in a manner incompatible with your style. Presenting a long list of principles may be a difficult memory task for analytical students, who try to memorize each relationship. For global learners the same task may tap conceptual reorganization skill rather than memorization skill.

Rather than try to *change* your style (a difficult undertaking), you should try to *transcend* it—to be aware of your style, to know its strengths, and, more importantly, to know its weaknesses.

Learning style	Weaknesses	Recommended processes
Deep global	• Not attending to important details	• Selecting (highlighting)
Deep analytic	• Not connecting and integrating information	• Perceiving structure • Abstracting themes
Surface global	• Not seeking underlying relationships and meaning	• Abstracting themes • Making sense of information
Surface analytic	• Not connecting information • Not seeking underlying relationships and meaning	• Perceiving structure • Abstracting themes • Making sense of information

Learn to attend to the type of information you tend to overlook.

Putting it together

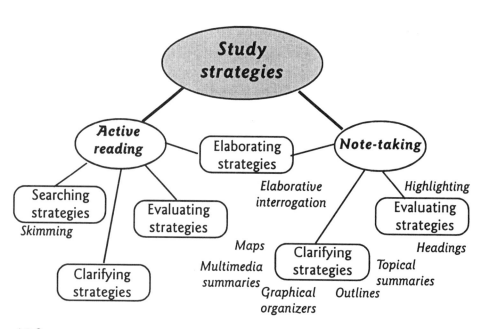

Main Ideas

❧ Study strategies are valuable to the extent that they help you understand the information and distinguish the important information from the less important.

❧ The first step to understanding is reading effectively. Effective reading requires the reader to be actively involved with the text.

❧ To help you select the important information, you must take notes effectively. Effective note-taking needs to be in your own words.

❧ To link new information with old, you need to go beyond the information presented (elaboration). Asking "why" questions is an effective means.

Answers to exercises:

9.3:

theme: country

alternative theme: farmwork

9.4:

The first connects the two nouns with a conjunction, the second with a locational preposition, and the third with an interactive preposition. The third is more memorable—not because it's funnier, but because it's interactive.

In the first list the noun pairs sound the same. In the second, they look the same. In the third, they are meaningfully connected.

CHAPTER 10

AN ANALYSIS OF MEMORY "TRICKS"

Memory "tricks"—mnemonic strategies—are very effective, but little used. Their cost is high, compared to preferred, less effective, strategies such as rote repetition, and more reliable strategies such as writing the information down. Mnemonic strategies are potentially valuable adjuncts to other learning strategies, and are most valuable for rote memorizing of facts.

Mnemonic strategies: What are they and do they work?

Aids to memory such as acronyms, rhymes, linking information by creating visual images or making up a story, are called mnemonics. They tend to be regarded as memory 'tricks" rather than memory strategies, but this is being unfair to them. As much as any other memory strategy, mnemonic strategies are built on the basic memory principles.

Mnemonic strategies are a special type of memory strategy.

One reason for the low status of mnemonics is that they are effective for rote memorization, but of little help in building understanding. However, although understanding is a necessary part of developing expertise, every subject has a core of information that must be learned by heart. And in daily life there are many facts that we need to know, but do not need to understand.

The Bottom Line
Mnemonic strategies are effective, but few people use them often. Why not?
⇒ Mnemonics take more time and effort to master than the preferred alternatives: external strategies, and rote repetition.
⇒ People don't know when to use them.

Mnemonic strategies have been recommended as appropriate for remembering the following types of information:

- Vocabulary.
- Shopping lists.
- Appointments.
- Cards.
- Speeches.
- Facts.
- Jokes.

- Names and faces.
- Phone numbers.
- Birthdays and anniversaries.
- Content of articles, books.
- Ideas.
- Dramatic parts and poems.
- Personal numbers (e.g., social security number; bank account number).

The limitations of mnemonics are no reason for discarding them. But to use them effectively you must be able to use them *judiciously*— to judge wisely when their use is advised.

To do that, you need to understand how the various strategies work.

Imagery mnemonics

Visual imagery underlies most mnemonic strategies. The best known are the *list-learning strategies—the place method*, the *pegword method*, and the *link method*. While these are undoubtedly effective strategies, they perhaps have less value as general strategic tools than the *transformational elaborative strategies—the keyword method*, and *face-name association*.

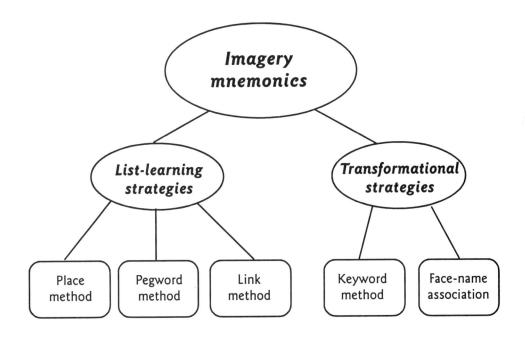

The keyword method

The keyword method has been especially pushed as an effective strategy for learning foreign vocabulary. It is presumably equally valuable for extending your native-language vocabulary and learning technical jargon, and has also been used successfully to teach social studies facts (e.g., the products of a country, capital cities), science facts (e.g., chemical reactions, parts of the skeletal and nervous systems) and the names and faces of people.

There are two stages to the method:

•◆ Link the foreign word with an English word that sounds like some part of the foreign word (e.g., the Spanish *carta* sounds like the English "cart"). This (cart) is the *keyword*.

•◆ Link the keyword with the English meaning of the foreign word by forming an interactive image (e.g., *carta* means "letter," so you could visualize a letter inside a cart).

The keyword method appears to be the most effective means of acquiring vocabulary for comprehension (understanding what a word means when you come across it), but if your goal is an ability to produce the word, rote repetition is better. In other words, your letter in the cart will help you remember what *carta* means when you come across it, but it won't necessarily help you recall the Spanish word for letter.

Similarly, if you learn that Canberra is the capital of Australia by visualizing a can on top of a map of Australia, you should find it easy to answer, "What is Canberra the capital of?," but less easy to answer, "What is the capital of Australia?."

The problem is that, although the keyword component of the word is much more likely to be recalled (the *cart* part of *carta*; the *can* part of *Canberra*), any word with that component seems equally possible.

Just think about it. To remember that *carta* means "letter" you need to:

1. Derive the keyword from the word (*cart* from *carta*).

2. Derive the interactive image from the keyword (*letter in cart* from *cart*).

3. Derive the meaning from the image (*letter*, from *letter in cart*).

Although this sounds somewhat complicated, this three-step process is merely repeating the steps by which you originally encoded the information. Clearly, the more obvious your original encoding, the easier it will be to recreate the process (*cart* is an obvious keyword for *carta*; *pet* is not quite so obvious for *pequenos*).

However, to remember the Spanish word for letter, you must:

1. Retrieve the interactive image (*letter in cart*, from *letter*).

2. Use the image to derive the keyword (*cart*, from *letter in cart*).

3. Use the keyword to derive the foreign word (*carta* from *cart*).

While *carta* might seem easily derived from *cart*, other associations are not likely to be so easy—imagine trying to derive *pequenos* from *pet* or *peck*.

> **The keyword method is very effective for
> linking a new fact to a well-learned fact,
> but is little help in recalling
> the new fact itself.**

Generally, however, comprehension is the main goal, and for this the keyword method is very effective. The main advantage of the keyword mnemonic over other strategies for remembering information of this type is that you acquire the information *faster*. But not better. Learning new words in a meaningful context is an equally effective strategy for long-term recall.

The keyword method: guide to use
⇒ Very effective for learning the meanings of words.

⇒ Not particularly effective for remembering the words themselves.

⇒ Most effective when you are supplied with the keyword, but create your own image.

⇒ Particularly suited for learning:

–vocabulary.

–face-name associations.

–core facts.

Face-name associations

A variant of the keyword method that is used more than other mnemonic strategies is that of face-name associations.

Because face-name associations are usually only required one way—remembering a name on seeing a face, rather than the other way around—an appropriately modified keyword method would seem potentially more suitable for face-name associations than it is for language learning.

Creating a face-name association:

⇒ Select a distinctive feature of the face (nose).

⇒ Select a word or phrase that sounds like the name (*con rat* for *Conrad*).

⇒ Create an interactive image linking the distinctive feature with the keyword(s) (a man in a prisoner's uniform—*con*—rides a *rat* that slides down the nose

To remember the name on seeing the face again, you must:

⇒ Identify the distinctive feature that you used when encoding (*nose*).

⇒ Use that feature to help you retrieve the interactive image (a *con* riding a *rat* sliding down a *nose*).

⇒ Derive the keyword(s) from the image (*con rat*).

⇒ Use the keyword to help you retrieve the name (*Conrad*).

As we have discussed, the connection between a person's name and their looks is entirely arbitrary—which is why the focus of the face-name association strategy is on forging a connection between physical features and the name (via visually-derived semantic codes).

The distinctive feature is pivotal to the success of the method. Without a distinctive feature the method doesn't work. The more distinctive the feature, the more effective the method will be. But most faces are not that distinctive! It's often hard to select a distinctive feature. And it's even harder to find a distinctive feature you haven't used frequently before.

**Face-name association works well to the
extent that the selected distinctive feature is
an effective cue.**

Most people find the strategy too difficult and time-consuming to apply in most social situations. With a great deal of practice you can, of course, become skilled at the method. But if you do not have a natural facility for this strategy, and you are not prepared to put in a great deal of practice, you are unlikely to find this a useful strategy for frequent use.

Although not quite so effective, a much easier strategy which will still considerably improve your recall of people's names, involves simply repeating the person's name as often as you can: when you are introduced, during conversation and when you say goodbye.

That is not to say that face-name association is not worth having in your tool-box. If remembering people's names is a priority for you, then it is certainly worth putting some time into practicing this strategy. Even if you lack the skill to use the strategy regularly, you can still master it sufficiently well for use when remembering a particular name is important enough for you to put in some effort.

However, the main value of the face-name association strategy is in situations where you have a large number of names to learn and the time to learn them. For example, a teacher could use this method to learn the names of all the students on the first day of class (provided the teacher has time to sit quietly and stare at the students!). If you are in a situation where you have a large number of names to learn, photographs of the people would enable you to apply this strategy in your own time.

List-learning strategies: the place method; the pegword method; and the link method

The *place method* (the method of loci, as it is traditionally known) is the classic mnemonic strategy, having its first recorded use 2500 years ago.

First of all, you choose a place you know very, very well. You might use a familiar route, your house, or a particular room in it. The crucial thing is that you can easily call to mind various "landmarks" (different fixed objects in a room, for example). These landmarks are your anchors. You must train yourself to go around your landmarks in a particular order. With a route of course, that is easy.

To remember a list, say a shopping list, you simply imagine each item in turn at these landmarks. For example, a loaf of bread sticking out of the letterbox; a giant apple in place of the door; the hall full of beans; a giant banana in the bath, etc.

This technique is extremely effective for learning lists. Not surprisingly, for it obeys two of our fundamental principles:

- It uses over-learned cues to anchor new information, and

- It uses visual imagery to strengthen the links.

Because the place method uses cues that are already well known to you, it is probably the easiest of the imagery mnemonics to master.

The place method is particularly appropriate and effective for waiting staff who go from table to table to take drink orders. Visualizing the drinks in particular locations is more effective than writing the orders down, probably because the time pressure in that kind of situation make an internal strategy more effective than an external one.

The *pegword method* is based on the same sort of idea as the place method, but instead of using locations as cues, it uses numbers. These numbers are transformed into visual images by means of the following simple rhyme: "One is a bun, two is a shoe, three is a tree, four is a door, five is a hive, six is sticks, seven is heaven, eight is a gate, nine is a line, and ten is a hen."

The rhyme must be learned by rote until it is over-learned. Accordingly, there is a higher "cost" to the pegword method than to the place method, where cues already over-learned are used. It does, however, have an advantage over the place method, in that the items learned are not tied to a particular sequence, and therefore it's not necessary to recall the whole list to retrieve a single item.

Like the place method and the pegword method, the *link method* uses visual images to link items together. However, instead of a well-learned structure to anchor the new information, items are linked to each other. For example, to remember our shopping list of bread, apples, beans, and bananas, you would form an image of the bread interacting with apples in some way, then another image of apples and beans, then another image bringing beans and bananas together. The items are thus chained together.

Major limitations of these methods:

⇒ *Place and Link Methods.* If you merely want to recall an item from the list, rather than needing to recall the whole list, you still need to start from the beginning and go through in order until you reach the item you want.

⇒ *Place and Pegword Methods.* By using the landmarks again and again, you can only readily recall the last list. Earlier lists are much less easily recalled. The technique is therefore of value only as a relatively short-term memory strategy—not as a way of acquiring permanent knowledge.

⇒ *All Methods.* The methods are difficult to use if the information is presented to you too fast.

⇒ *Pegword and Link Methods.* The methods are difficult to use effectively without extensive training.

Most people have a limited need to learn lists. Mnemonic list-learning strategies have a greater potential usefulness when used in conjunction with other strategies.

> **Mnemonic list-learning strategies can be**
> **useful in conjunction with other strategies.**

The advantages of mnemonic list-learning strategies:

⇒ They can organize information in memory.

⇒ They can provide anchors for information.

⇒ They can strengthen links.

If you remember the emphasis I have placed on the need for anchors—those key bits of information that serve as reference points for a cluster—it will be apparent that mnemonic list-learning strategies have the potential to be an effective means of encoding those anchors for easy recall.

There are two main kinds of textual material for which mnemonic strategies are particularly appropriate:

•• Text that is readily understandable but which contains a number of details that might be overlooked.

•• Text that is structured, but is not sufficiently well-known or well-organized for the structure to be used as a frame for retrieval.

To use a list-learning strategy for text:
1. *Understand* the information.
2. *Select* the anchors.
3. *Encode* the anchors (mnemonic).
4. *Cluster* the encoded anchors (mnemonic).

For your anchors you should select details you suspect you wouldn't otherwise remember, or details that would serve as effective cues for other bits of information. You encode those details by creating a visual image for them, and then integrate the details using the list-learning mnemonic—say, the place method.

The use of a mnemonic list-learning strategy in such a manner is of demonstrated effectiveness.

A warning: Mastering a subject requires you to acquire a large number of facts and new vocabulary, and accordingly, mnemonic strategies would seem potentially effective means of acquiring these basics. However, being an expert is not simply a matter of "knowing a lot." An expert has a well-organized domain into which new information can be easily integrated. Mnemonic techniques on their own do not help you understand the meaning of facts, and do not therefore help you develop expertise in a subject.

List-learning strategies: guide to use
⇒ To be used effectively, you need to be able to create images quickly.

⇒ To be used effectively, all steps need to be properly implemented.

⇒ They help you learn faster, not better.

⇒ They are useful for:

  −learning the right order.

  −memorizing retrieval cues.

  −anchoring many details.

⇒ They are trivially useful for:

  −shopping lists.

Using imagery

Most mnemonic strategies are based on imagery. There is no doubt that imagery can be an effective tool, but there is nothing particularly special about imagery. The advantage of imagery is that it provides an easy way of connecting information that is not otherwise readily connected. However, providing verbal links (see *story method* below) is equally effective.

The critical element is that words or images provide a context which links the information. Thus, imagery is only effective when it is an *interactive* image: one that ties together one bit of information with another.

Visual imagery on its own is of limited value without an organizing structure, such as the place or pegword methods.

It is usually emphasized that bizarre images are remembered much better, but there is no evidence for this. Indeed, in many studies, ordinary images are remembered slightly better. One of the problems is that most people find it harder to create bizarre images. Unless you have a natural talent for thinking up bizarre images, it is probably not worth bothering with.

Imagery: points to remember

⇒ Images are effective to the extent that they link information.

⇒ Images are not inherently superior to words.

⇒ Bizarre images are not necessarily recalled better than common images.

⇒ Imagery is chiefly effective when used with an organizing structure.

Exercise 10.1

Here are some items from a visual imagery questionnaire to help you rate your ability to visualize. (The items are taken from Marks' Vividness of Visual Imagery Questionnaire).

In this exercise, there are a total of eight images. Rate each image on the scale of one to five, according to whether it is:

Perfectly clear and as vivid as normal vision.	1
Clear and reasonably vivid.	2
Moderately clear and vivid.	3
Vague and dim.	4
No image, you only "know" that you are thinking of the subject.	5

Think of some relative or friend whom you frequently see (but who is not with you at present) and consider carefully the picture that comes before your mind's eye. Rate each of the following images according to the scale.

1. The exact contour of face, head, shoulders, and body.
2. Characteristic poses of head, attitudes of body etc.
3. The precise carriage, length of step, etc. in walking.
4. The different colors worn in some familiar clothes.

Visualize a rising sun. Consider carefully the picture that comes before your mind's eye.

5. The sun is rising above the horizon into a hazy sky.
6. The sky clears and surrounds the sun with blueness.
7. Clouds. A storm blows up, with flashes of lightning.
8. A rainbow appears.

Add up the total of your rating scores and divide by 8 to get your average score. An average of over 3 suggests you are a good visualizer, while an average below 2 indicates a poor visualizer.

Verbal mnemonics

Main points about verbal mnemonics:
⇒ Coding mnemonics are the most effective means of memorizing numbers.
⇒ Coding mnemonics can be used to dramatically extend the value of the pegword method.
⇒ First-letter mnemonics are most effective for learning the *order* of well-learned information.
⇒ First-letter mnemonics can be useful for overcoming memory blocks.
⇒ The story method is a very effective means of learning lists.

The emphasis on visual imagery in mnemonics reflects in part the low level of literacy through most of human history. Methods that use words rather than images have been shown to be equally effective. Imagery has one major advantage, and that is the ease with which two items can be connected using imagery. Imagery also has one major disadvantage, and that is the difficulty most people have with creating images.

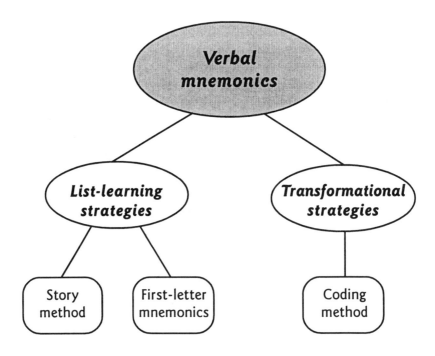

Coding mnemonics

Coding Mnemonics: Guide to Use
- A very effective means of remembering numbers.
- Crucial for making the pegword method a valuable tool.

Coding mnemonics are used for encoding numbers. Because words are much easier for most of us to remember, a system that transforms numbers into letters is one of the best ways for remembering numbers.

Here is one such coding system:

1 = t (there is *1* downstroke in *t*)

2 = n (there are *2* downstrokes in *n*)

3 = m (there are *3* downstrokes in *m*)

4 = r (*r* is the last letter of *four*)

5 = l (*l* is 50 in Roman numbers)

6 = sh (*six* has a sort of *sh* sound)

7 = k (number *7* is embedded in *k*)

8 = f (both *8* and *f* have two loops)

9 = p (*9* is an upside-down *p*)

0 = s (*zero* starts with a *s* sound)

The codes are not arbitrary. They have been chosen with a view to facilitating rote memorization. As you can see, however, some of the rationales are somewhat contrived.

If you want to have a coding strategy in your tool-box, you are not obliged to memorize a coding system that is given to you. There is no particular superiority in any one set of digit-letter equivalences over another. But if you are modifying a coding system by substituting equivalences you find more obvious, you need to bear in mind confusability. For example, an equivalence between *f* and *5* might seem obvious, but there is a strong likelihood of becoming confused between *4* and *5* when decoding.

Once encoded into letters, the numbers can then be incorporated into words or rhymes. For example, World War Two ended in 1945—*tprl*, which could be turned into *top role*. (Only consonants are used for coding. Vowels are then inserted as necessary.)

The modern innovation of encoding phone numbers into letters (800-ANNSETT) is a useful descendent of this strategy.

A coding system is very useful for remembering numbers, but it must be said that few people have sufficient need to memorize long numbers to make the initial cost of learning the code acceptable. There are exceptions of course. You may have a job where the memorization of many prices, quantities, or measurements is required or desirable, for example. But for most of us, written and electronic records are preferable, being far less costly and more reliable. The advent of smart telephones has, of course, made our need to memorize phone numbers much less.

Of course, such records have their disadvantages. They are not always available when you require them, and they may be lost or destroyed. How important those dangers are is a matter for the individual to decide.

The coding system has another value: that of supplying pegs for the pegword system. By allowing numbers to be encoded as easily remembered words, the number of pegs can be extended from 10 to infinity. For example, the pegword for 22 could be *nun*. Lists of such pegwords are available in various memory improvement books.

Clearly of course, mastery of such a system requires a very large investment of time and effort, as well as a facility for image creation. But if you decide that the pegword strategy is for you, you should certainly increase its value by learning a coding system.

Such systems have been suggested for memorizing such information as appointments, and birthdays, and anniversaries. There is no evidence that mnemonic strategies are particularly effective for tasks in the planning memory domain and most people find external strategies—diaries, calendars, watch alarms—more dependable and easier to use.

Humor is, of course, replete with instances of people (usually men) forgetting birthdays and anniversaries, but I suspect that any person sufficiently motivated to use a mnemonic strategy for this purpose would be sufficiently motivated to remember without use of such aids.

A person who would find an extended pegword system of the greatest value is one who intends to use it regularly as a means of encoding anchors for "factual" information, or one who has an unusual need to memorize numbers.

Exercise 10.2

Transform the following into their letter codes and make up a memorable word or phrase:

04-489-6535

Oct. 21, 1963

4 p.m., February 6

0062534-25

First letter mnemonics

Guide to Use. First-letter mnemonics:

⇒ Are a cueing strategy, not a learning strategy.

⇒ Are useful when remembering the order is critical, or

⇒ When you want to prevent a memory block.

First-letter mnemonics are probably the most widely used mnemonic. This reflects the popularity of specific mnemonics, rather than its wide use as a strategic tool.

There are two types of first-letter mnemonic: *acronyms* in which the initial letters form a meaningful word—such as FACE for the notes in the spaces of the treble staff—and *acrostics* in which the initial letters are used as the initial letters of other words to make a meaningful phrase—such as *E*very *G*ood *B*oy *D*eserves *F*ruit for the notes on the lines of the treble staff.

Medical students tend to rely heavily on such mnemonics to help them master anatomical details, such as the names of the cranial nerves: **On Old Olympia's Towering Top A Finn And German Vault And Hop** (olfactory, optic, oculomotor, trochlear, trigeminal, abducens, facial, auditory, glossopharyngeal, vagus, accessory, and hypoglossal). This demonstrates the major limitation of this method; its value is entirely in serving as a reminder of information that is already very well-learned. Learning this phrase would not help most of us remember the cranial nerves, because the nerves themselves are not sufficiently familiar to us. ROYGBIV helps us recall the colors of the spectrum, in the correct order, because the names of the colors are already well-known to us.

> **Learning a first-letter mnemonic does not help you learn the information being cued by the mnemonic. For the mnemonic phrase to be an effective cue, the information being cued must be well learned.**

This brings us to the chief use of this method. First letter mnemonics are a very effective means of recalling the *order* of well-learned items. First letter mnemonics are a *cueing strategy*; they remind us of what we already know. They are therefore particularly effective as a means to overcome memory blocks—for example, for students whose minds "go blank" in exams.

They can of course, lead to errors when more than one item shares the same first letter. The acrostic for cranial nerves, for example, contains three Os, two Ts and two As. As with image formation, some people find it harder to think up acrostics than others (one student reportedly took 20 minutes to make up one six-letter phrase!)

The story method

The story method is another list-learning strategy. It is the verbal equivalent of the link method. Items are chained together by linking them in a story. For example, here is a story a student created to remember the capitalized items: A VEGETABLE can be a useful INSTRUMENT for a COLLEGE student. A carrot can be a NAIL for your FENCE or BASIN. But a MERCHANT of the QUEEN would SCALE that fence and feed the carrot to a GOAT.

The story method is as effective as the imagery methods for learning lists. Which one will be most effective for you depends on which type of information (words or images) you deal with most easily.

Mnemonic strategies:
What are they good for?

Traditionally, education has involved the rote memorization of facts. In modern times this focus has been justly deplored, and emphasis has been placed instead on the importance of *understanding* information. As is common with revolutions, the reaction has perhaps been excessive. It is not true that all information is meaningful. It is not true that only information that can be understood is worth learning. My father's birthday is worth my while learning, but it is not meaningful. There is no meaningful connection between a person's name and that person's face. The color-coding of electric wires is not something that can be understood.

Certainly information that is meaningful should be learned in a meaningful way, but information which is not meaningful or integrated (or potentially so) needs to be learned in a different way. The principles of learning, however, apply to all information. Meaning and organization always aid recall. Effective retrieval cues are always critical. To improve your recall of unrelated information therefore, you need to find some way of supplying meaning, organization, and effective cues.

Mnemonics are the most effective way of doing that.

Mnemonics:

⇒ Provide a structure on which to anchor information.

⇒ Connect otherwise unrelated information.

But the cost of most mnemonic strategies is high. And higher for some people than others. For most tasks, there are less costly strategies which, though perhaps less effective, are sufficiently effective to be preferable for many people. The principal alternatives to mnemonic strategies are: written or electronic records, and rote repetition.

For many tasks and for most people, a written list is far less effort, far more likely to be used, and far more reliable.

Some people feel that they are unable to use a list effectively because they always forget to take it. However, research has confirmed what many of us already know from experience: even if you forget to take your list, you are much more likely to recall items that you have written down. The act of writing (and perhaps the opportunity to visualize your list) are sufficient to improve your memory.

The chief advantage of a mnemonic strategy over the much less costly alternative of writing a list is that it can help you remember those items which you recall at times when writing materials are not available (such as while driving). This is why proponents of mnemonic strategies sometimes suggest that mnemonics can help you remember ideas. More than most types of information, ideas are something that often come to us in situations where writing them down is not an option, or at least inconvenient—in bed, out walking, in a car, talking to someone.

One of the more valuable uses of a mnemonic list-learning strategy is as an aid to remembering a speech or presentation. A mnemonic strategy has three main advantages over the preferred alternative strategy of written notes: written notes can be lost or left behind; looking down at written notes breaks your rapport with the audience; referring to written notes can break your flow.

Mnemonics have also sometimes been suggested as an aid to remembering dramatic parts. Information such as this needs to be remembered verbatim, and there is no real substitute for rote repetition. However, some people have found mnemonic list-learning strategies helpful as an adjunct to this strategy, to provide them with retrieval cues signaling what comes next. Mnemonic strategies are, of course, excellent for the purpose of signaling the order of well-learned information.

Looking at our list of 10 memory tasks given in chapter 1, we can see that mnemonic strategies can be useful in half those tasks. They aren't, as a general rule, particularly appropriate for information in the planning memory domain, or the event memory domain. In the case of the first task (remembering information you have studied), mnemonic strategies are most useful as an adjunct to other strategies.

Memory task	Mnemonic Strategy
Remembering information you have studied.	Keyword method; list-learning strategies.
Remembering someone's name/face.	Face-name associations.
Remembering important dates.	Coding mnemonic.
Remembering details about another person.	N/A
Remembering to do something.	N/A
Remembering when/where something happened.	N/A
Remembering whether you've done something.	N/A
Remembering where you've put something.	N/A
Remembering the names of things.	Keyword method.
Remembering how to do something.	List-learning strategies.

Exercise 10.3

Read the following descriptions of some memory situations, and choose an appropriate mnemonic strategy.

1. You're a sales representative and you want to impress your customers by remembering the details of previous purchases without referring to a piece of paper. What memory strategy do you use?

2. You call directory assistance from a public phone, then find the number you want is busy and you will have to remember it for several minutes, if not longer. You are without anything to write with. What do you use to remember it?

3. You are going to a function at your partner's workplace and you ask your partner to remind you of the names and roles of the various people she works with. How do you remember them?

4. You're a waiter and want to remember what the people at various tables have ordered without constantly referring to your list. What strategy do you use?

5. Your boss calls you over and gives you a number of instructions. How do you ensure you remember them all?

Putting it together

Mnemonic strategies are:

Most effective for remembering information with a short use-by date.

Excellent for cueing well-learned information (for overcoming memory blocks; for reminding you of the order of information).

Useful for encoding anchors.

Most useful when written records are impossible, inconvenient, or inappropriate.

Written records are more appropriate when:

You need to remember the information for a long time.

When reliability and accuracy are important.

When memory load is to be avoided.

When information is coming at you too quickly.

When the information is too complex.

Main Ideas

ↀ Mnemonic strategies are an effective means of memorizing facts, but not for building understanding.

ↀ The keyword method is an effective strategy for learning the *meaning* of words, but not for remembering the word itself.

ↀ Face-name association is effective for remembering people's names if you are skilled at selecting distinctive facial features and forming images.

ↀ The place, pegword and link methods all use visual images to make items in a list more memorable.

ↀ Mnemonic list-learning strategies are most valuable as a means of providing a retrieval structure.

∞ Words are potentially as effective as images, the critical factor is that the words or images link items together.

In general, mnemonics are useful for remembering lists of items, for pairing items, for the order of items.

Answers to exercises:

10.3:

1. Coding and pegword methods.
2. Coding mnemonic.
3. Keyword method.
4. Place method.
5. Link or story method.

———

CHAPTER 11
GENERAL SUPPORT STRATEGIES

Mnemonic strategies and traditional study skills are memory strategies that attempt to improve memory by manipulating the information to be remembered. Such memory strategies are very task specific, and the more skilled you become at a strategy of this type, the more narrow its application. Other memory strategies manipulate your attention via your physical condition, your emotional state, your attitude, the physical environment, or the social environment. These are less task specific than strategies that manipulate information, and most of them need to be employed considerably ahead of the time when they are needed.

Information manipulation strategies

Information manipulation strategies are task specific. Strategies such as mnemonics are indeed *very* specific. A first-letter mnemonic is best suited to a word list, not for text, nor for remembering a face. The place method is best suited for learning single-item lists, while interactive imagery is best for paired items. Not only are most memory strategies extremely task-specific, but they actually become *more* specific as you become more skilled at them (something of a Catch-22). A strategy that *loses* specificity requires *more* attention (and is therefore more costly).

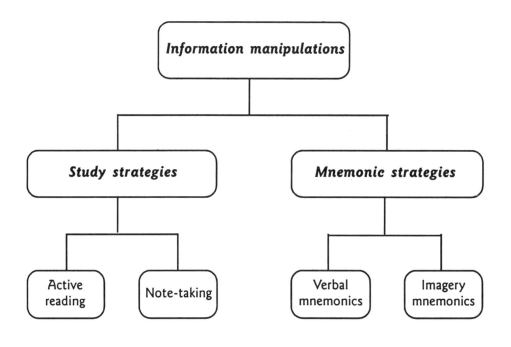

Because of the specificity of information-manipulation strategies, some researchers have concluded that you cannot satisfactorily improve your memory on the basis of these skills alone. More general strategies are also needed.

General support strategies

We have spent a lot of time looking at understanding and selecting information. It is time we looked at the third leg of our tripod: attention.

Instead of manipulating information to make it easier to remember, general support strategies manipulate your ability to process information. They do this primarily through their effect on your attention.

There are two aspects to improving attention: the first is about improving the *quality* of your attention. The second is about improving the *direction* of your attention.

Paying attention

Although everyone agrees that "paying attention" is critical in improving your learning and remembering, there is very little evidence for it. This is partly because no one really understands what attention is, and partly because the effectiveness of training programs to improve attentiveness has not been properly assessed.

The following elements have been suggested as important in improving the quality and focus of your attention:

- Eliminating distractions (external and internal).

- Limiting how long you concentrate.

- Setting deadlines.

- Establishing goals.

- Increasing motivation.

Remembering that we are limited in the amount of information we can work with at one time, I would add to this list:

- Limiting the amount of information you try to process at one time.

Let's look first at those strategies designed to direct your attention appropriately. Remember, however well you are concentrating, it does little good if you are attending to the wrong information!

Planning skills

Setting goals

Goal-setting is fundamental to effective encoding:

- To deciding the proper strategy.

- To properly directing your attention.

- To the effective management of your time.

There are two aspects to setting goals wisely. The first relates to how well you articulate your goal, the second to the type of goal. I have already defined the fundamental principle of effective goal-setting (in the context of effective retrieval searches):

Make your goal as specific as possible.

Not only is it easier to assess whether you have defined your goal accurately when you have defined it specifically, but it is also easier to judge whether the goal is realistic. Thus, aiming to learn all the faces and names of the people at your new workplace within a week is a much better goal than aiming to "get better at putting names to faces."

In specifying your goal, it helps if you also establish what you *don't* need to know. This helps limit your search, and allows you to focus on what you do need to know.

Part of specifying your goal concerns the level of mastery you want to achieve. For example, you might only want to learn enough to pass a test. The level of mastery depends also on how long you want to remember the information. If the test is the next day, you will put in less effort than if the test is next week. Similarly, if you simply want to remember the names of people at your partner's workplace long enough not to embarrass yourself at a particular function, you will adopt a different strategy than if you want to remember their names for an indefinite period. Goals may be either *process goals*, or *outcome goals*. As its name suggests, an outcome goal defines your objective in terms of achieving a particular outcome (e.g., to learn to drive a car, to read a chapter, to spend four hours studying). Process goals refer to specific steps on the way to achieving that outcome (thus a process goal for learning to drive a car might be to learn to start the car smoothly).

In general, process goals appear to be more effective than outcome goals. However, the best strategy seems to be to work towards process goals in the early stages of learning a skill, but once the components have been mastered, to work towards an outcome goal.

For example, in a study of dart throwing, novices who were told to concentrate on properly executing the last two (specified) steps in every throw, did better than those who were told to concentrate on achieving a high numeric score. But the most accomplished novices were those who were first told to concentrate on those process goals and then, when they had mastered those, were told to concentrate on achieving a high score. Not only did this flexible strategy result in better mastery of the skill, but also greater interest and satisfaction. Similarly, successful writers and academics (who tend to have long deadlines and little feedback) often use sub-goals such as daily output charts to help them work towards a distant outcome goal such as finishing a book.

Part of the reason for the greater effectiveness of process goals may simply relate to their greater specificity. Specificity may also be the reason why the use of process goals seems to result in users being less likely to see poor performance as due to a lack of ability. Instead they (rightly) see it as a failure to master a particular skill, probably through insufficient practice. Setting a number of process goals also gives you intermediate objectives that can provide a framework for a system of small rewards to yourself.

Principles of effective goal-setting:

⇒ Specify both your desired outcome and intermediate steps on the way.

⇒ Make the intermediate goals as specific as possible.

⇒ Ensure the goal is specified in such a way that you will know when you have achieved it.

Exercise 11.1

What is your goal in reading this book? Can you specify the sub-goals you have developed during the course of reading this book (e.g., to master the face-name association strategy) and the specific steps you will need to perform (e.g., to think up distinctive features for a specified set of people)? Are these process goals specific enough that you will recognize when you have achieved them?

Managing your time

One characteristic of less successful students is that they tend not to appropriately manage their time. Instead of allocating time on the basis of the difficulty of the information to be learned, they tend to spend *more* time on material that is easier to understand, and *less* time on material that is difficult. Successful learners, on the other hand, are much better at assessing the difficulty of material and appropriately managing their efforts.

Effective learners commonly use specific strategies for managing their study time, such as:
⇒ Scheduling a particular, regular time for study.
⇒ Setting specific output goals.
⇒ Using environmental aids such as alarms and appointment books.

———

The actual level of your goal is an important determinant of how long you spend studying: someone aiming for a 90 percent grade on a test usually spends a lot longer than someone just "doing their best." But while it is important to *manage* your time, time should not be used as a goal—for example, by saying that you will spend four hours studying. To use your time wisely, it must be considered in conjunction with process and outcome goals.

To develop your time-management skills, you first have to become aware of how you spend your time. Keeping a log of your activities at 30-minute intervals for a week is usually a real eye-opener! Then you need to develop a realistic appreciation of how much you can achieve in a particular time-period.

To develop a better feel for how long it takes to encode.
Before starting a learning task, jot down the following:
⇒ How much time do you think the task will take?
⇒ What steps are involved in reaching the goal?

At the end of the task, answer the following:

⇒ Did you have enough time?
Too much time?

⇒ Was the task more complex that you had thought?

⇒ How would you approach it in future?

After you have done this a number of times, you will start to develop a better sense of what goals and time frames are realistic.

Conditions for effective time-wmanagement

⇒ Setting of specific and realistic goals.

⇒ Setting of realistic time allotments.

⇒ Belief in the value of time-management strategies.

⇒ Faith in your control over events.

Monitoring skills

A critical factor behind effective learners' superior time management skills is their better *monitoring* skills. If you don't realize that you haven't learned something adequately (and this is frequently true), then you are unlikely to devote any more time to it.

In most cases, people stop studying long before they have reached the desired level of mastery of the material. There are a number of reasons for this:

• Faulty knowledge of how long it takes to properly incorporate new information.

• Failure to properly check recall.

• Failure to understand the material, without realizing they don't understand it.

• Lack of time.

• Lack of motivation.

Part of the problem many people have with knowing how long it will take them to properly encode some particular information is their poor judgment of how difficult the information is. Like any other skill, judging item difficulty is a skill that needs well-directed practice.

Perhaps because the difficulty of specific items is much easier to judge than the difficulty of broad ideas, your awareness of how well you know something tends to be better for specific details.

An important component of monitoring your learning is testing your memory. While people are very consistent about their judgements of what information they hold in store ("I can't remember it right now, but I know I know it"), they are not actually very accurate, particularly when the information is difficult. Thus your opinion that you have learned something is not, in itself, worth a great deal.

But even people who bother to test their memory for newly encoded information do not necessarily do it right. For example, if you test your *recognition* of the information rather than your ability to *recall* it, you will get an inflated idea of how much you know. Less obviously, if you test your recall too soon after encoding, you will also over-rate your grasp of the information. To adequately test whether new information has been properly incorporated into your database, you need to try and recall it some considerable time later.

You can monitor either time or goals. But monitoring time can have a hindering effect, by diverting attention away from what, after all, is far more important: what you have accomplished, not how long you stared at your books. Monitoring performance on specific goals, by directing attention appropriately, is usually better. But goal setting, time management and monitoring cannot be considered independent of each other. Efficient time management involves setting realistic goals. Realistic goal setting requires you to take the amount of time available into consideration. Monitoring is at its best when it measures performance against both time and goals.

Your monitoring skills are not determined by your general competence, nor by your expertise in a particular area, but they are likely to be affected by your personality. Impulsive people, in particular, are likely to be poor at monitoring.

Monitoring involves the following strategies:

⇒ Matching answers to initial questions.

⇒ Checking performance against goals

⇒ Revising: re-drafting or recalculation or even setting revised goals.

⇒ Testing recall.

Strategies to improve the quality of attention

Manipulating your environment

Physical environment

There are a number of ways you can manipulate your physical environment to help improve your remembering:

- Structuring your environment for better concentration. (For example, some people find a certain level of background noise helps them concentrate, whereas others need complete quiet. Extremes of temperature also impair memory, but within those limits there will be a temperature range that is optimal for *you*. What is important is that (a) you structure your environment to suit *you*, and (b) you use that environment consistently.

- Attempting to match the retrieval environment with the environment in which you originally encoded the information.

- Using an *environmental aid* to cue recall, such as:

  —Entering appointments in a diary or on a calendar.
  —Writing on the back of your hand.
  —Using clocks, oven timers, alarms on watches, etc.
  —Putting objects in a conspicuous place.
  —Putting a knot in your handkerchief.

Ⓞ────ₘ

When to use environmental aids:

⇒ When a number of interfering activities occur between encoding and recall (for example, having to remember to buy groceries after work).

⇒ When there is a long time between encoding and recall (for example, needing to make a doctor's appointment two months in the future).

⇒ When internal aids are not trusted to be sufficiently reliable (as when precise details need to be remembered) or when there is a strict time limit (when to check a cake in the oven, for example).

⇒ When memory load is to be avoided (as when you are attending to more than one activity).

─────

Social interaction

Much of our remembering occurs in social situations. Certainly the failures of memory that most embarrass us occur in situations that involve other people. This is not simply a matter of forgetting people's names and personal details, or forgetting a social engagement (although these instances account for a large part of the memory failures that bother us). We also are required to pick up a great deal of information from other people: in the context of meetings, seminars, instructions from bosses or clients, as well as casual conversation.

Embarrassment also results when we repeatedly recall the same information in a social situation.

Both encoding and retrieval problems can be helped by various social skills, in particular by conversational skills.

Ⓞ────ₘ

Encoding and retrieval can be helped by:

⇒ Restating what has just been said.

⇒ Keeping the conversation to a narrow focus.

⇒ Slowing the rate at which information is presented.

⇒ Asking questions to gain time.

⇒ Asking questions to elaborate information.

Manipulating yourself

Physical condition

By and large, improving your memory by improving your physical condition is about eliminating habits that impair memory. Your mind works better if you eat properly (not too much; not too little; the right sort of food), and get some exercise. It works better if not impaired by substances such as alcohol, tobacco, marijuana, some tranquilizers and sedatives, etc. Whether you can actually improve memory by becoming super-fit and healthy is much less clear.

A rather more interesting aspect of physical condition (because it doesn't depend on willpower) concerns sleep and your daily biological rhythm.

How time of day affects memory:

⇒ Retrieval is markedly worse in the first 20 minutes after waking.

⇒ The time of day doesn't affect your ability to retrieve information from the database.

⇒ In general, encoding is better done later in the day.

⇒ Improved encoding later in the day may be due to an increased ability to concentrate.

Emotional state

Intense emotion, depression, or stress can impair your memory—probably by making it more difficult to concentrate. While there is no evidence that using relaxation or meditation techniques as a matter of routine has any effect on learning (various claims notwithstanding), specific relaxation techniques (not simply telling yourself to relax!) can help on occasions when you are stressed or anxious.

As I have mentioned earlier, mood can also affect memory through its role in context. If your mood when retrieving information matches your mood when you originally encoded the information, it will be easier to recall.

Attitude

As touched on in chapter 1, you perform better when you believe in yourself and your skills. A person who believes they have a good memory already has an advantage over someone who believes they have a poor memory, regardless of how true those beliefs are.

Attitude can also affect your *selection* of information. We are less inclined to remember information that we disagree with or are uncomfortable with. We are more inclined to remember information that supports prejudices and beliefs we hold.

Putting it together

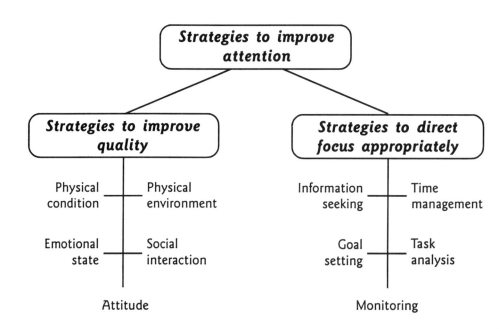

Main Ideas

To direct your attention appropriately:

- Precisely specify your goals.

- Learn to judge the difficulty of different encoding tasks.

- Specify how accessible you need the information to be and for how long.

- Manage your time.

- Check progress at regular intervals.

- Switch strategies when required.

To improve the quality of your attention:

- Structure your environment for better concentration.

- Control the rate of information through conversation skills.

- Schedule encoding periods for times of day at which you are most focused.

- Use effective relaxation techniques if required.

- Develop a positive belief in your memory skills.

Chapter 12

Becoming a Successful Strategy User

The key to improving your memory skills lies in developing a master strategy which enables you to flexibly and appropriately use the numerous memory skills in your repertoire. The ability to choose the right strategy for the task requires you not only to be practiced at making strategic decisions, but also that you master the specific skills in your repertoire to the level of a habit.

Your master strategy

The main difficulty in improving your memory is not the learning of specific memory strategies, but in learning which strategy is appropriate to use on a particular task.

You can acquire knowledge about when to use specific strategies through instruction, but you need to go beyond this. You need to develop your own rich knowledge of when different strategies work and don't work for you, by:

1. Comparing strategies with each other.

2. Assessing which is most effective in particular memory situations.

3. Remembering this information for later use.

⊖━━ₘ

A good strategy user:

⇒ Analyzes the task.

⇒ Notes similarities and differences with other tasks.

⇒ Assesses which strategies are most likely to be effective.

⇒ Tries out different strategies methodically.

⇒ Monitors each one's performance to determine whether it is indeed effective.

Matching memory tasks with appropriate strategies

To choose an appropriate strategy we need to understand the nature of the memory task. For example, outlining is an effective strategy when dealing with an expository text such as this one, but it wouldn't be useful if you were wanting to remember a folktale. Answering questions embedded in the text appears to help you remember a folktale, but not (oddly enough) an expository text.

Often, of course, more than one memory strategy is required in a situation. Thus, in encoding text, you might use summarization and elaboration, as well as a mnemonic strategy for specific details such as names.

The emphasis throughout most of this book has been on encoding—and rightly, because it is only through encoding effectively that you will achieve serious memory improvement. However, we must never forget that encoding and retrieving are reflections of each other.

**When you retrieve information, your strategy
must match the strategy used when the
information was encoded.**

Thus, if you originally learned the material using rhymes, then a rhyme cue is most likely to be effective. Similarly, if you are trying to remember an autobiographical event, you are best to search for those sorts of cues that usually mark such events: cues of activity, place, and people present.

The following table suggests appropriate strategies (some specific and some broad principles) for common memory tasks:

Memory task	Appropriate strategies
Information you have studied.	Study strategies; keyword method; mnemonic list-learning strategies.
Someone's name/face.	Attending to distinctive and unchangeable features; conversational strategies; face-name associations.
Important dates.	Coding mnemonic; external aids.
Details about another person.	Building strong links between structural and biographical codes and between biographical codes and related clusters.
To do something.	External aids; encoding trigger events.
When/where something happened.	Encoding distinctive features.
Whether you've done something.	Paying attention.
Where you've put something.	Paying attention.
Names of things.	Keyword method; repetition; seeking the meaning of names.
How to do something.	Practice; list-learning strategies; external aids.

Being a strategic thinker

Being a successful strategist requires more than a knowledge of good strategies and more than knowing when to use them (although these are both important). You need to become a *strategic thinker*.

A strategic thinker automatically sees a memory situation as requiring a strategy. For example, you heard on the car radio that the Dow Jones Industrial Average was up 37.5 points at 10,257 and that the NASDAQ was at 4,365.5, and you want to remember these details.

The naïve memorist would probably repeat these numbers over and over again and, because there are too many numbers and the person is engaged in another task (driving a car), would almost certainly lose most if not all of the information.

A person with some knowledge of mnemonic strategies might try to chunk the digits in a meaningful way, but, unless the person is particularly skilled at this, he or she will also probably lose much of the information. Again, this is because of the complexity of the information, the small amount of time allowed to encode the information, and the fact that the person is engaged in another task.

Strategic thinkers, on the other hand, would instantly realize the problems they are up against, and just as quickly identify the strategies needed to deal with the situation. They would then decide whether they possess the required internal strategy at the requisite level of skill (quite high in the particular circumstances), and if so, they would be employing it before the first number had finished.

The point is, in many common situations, your time to encode information is extremely limited. You do not have the luxury to sit and ponder and consult your notes. You must recognize instantly:

•◆ That you wish to remember something.

•◆ What information, exactly, you wish to remember.

•◆ The constraints of the situation.

•◆ Whether you in fact possess the requisite skills given the constraints of the situation.

•◆ Which strategy is appropriate.

In the above situation, a strategic thinker would have realized as soon as the stock market report came on that they would need to remember a number of figures. They would have realized that they would have very little time to encode the figures and that their attention would be divided. They would have probably decided that a pegword mnemonic would be the most appropriate strategy for encoding the numbers, and if they were confident of their mastery of this particular strategy, would have brought it to the forefront of their mind, ready to use it.

On the other hand, if they realized their skill was insufficient in these circumstances, they might have decided to follow an alternative strategy: pull over, and dig out a pen and paper. The point is, they would have made all these decisions almost instantly, because they were mentally prepared and practiced at analyzing memory situations.

Cutting your losses is an important part of thinking strategically.

You must develop your ability to recognize just how much information you can take away from a particular situation.

To estimate how much information you should select, you need to consider:

⇒ The rate of presentation.

⇒ The style of the information.

⇒ The density of the information.

⇒ Your level of related knowledge.

⇒ Your mood and receptivity.

The first step in becoming a strategic thinker then, is practicing your appraisal of memory situations. As with all memory strategies, you need to practice this strategy until its use is habitual and automatic if you want to achieve durable memory improvement.

Appraise the memory situation

The memory situation is something rather more than the memory task, although of course it includes the memory task.

To appraise the memory situation:

⇒ Analyze the memory task.

⇒ Articulate your goal.

⇒ Note the constraints of context.

For example, imagine that you have called directory assistance from a public phone for a long-distance number.

The task is an encoding one. It concerns remembering a number that is 10 digits long. The first three digits are meaningful (representing the area code, which you probably know). The other seven digits are not meaningful. The number is given to you verbally, usually once only. Your goal is to remember the number long enough to dial it. You have no need to remember it beyond that point. But you must remember it exactly. You are alone in a public place. You have no means of writing a number down and you have nobody available to help you remember the number.

On the basis of this analysis (which sounds long and complicated, but in fact is no more than we do many times daily without thinking), you will realize that your choice of strategies is between a mnemonic coding strategy and simple maintenance rehearsal. Unless you are very skilled at coding numbers, you will most probably opt for maintenance rehearsal.

However, if the situation changes—the line is busy and you have to remember the number for longer—you may reconsider your alternatives. If you can devise a mnemonic for the number (while holding it in working memory), you may now choose to do that. Or you may decide the most sensible thing is to go in search of a pen (while holding the data in working memory via rehearsal).

⊙——ᵐ

Analyze the task:

⇛ Is it a matter of encoding or retrieval?

⇛ What memory domain is involved?

⇛ Is the information meaningful?

⇛ How is the information presented?

Specify your goal:

⇛ What do you want the information for?

⇛ How long do you need to remember the information for?

⇛ How much detail do you need?

Note the constraints of context:

⇛ Are you under time pressure?

⇛ Are you alone or in a social or group setting?

⇛ Is your state of mind favorable to attention?

⇛ Are there environmental constraints?

Exercise 12.1

Analyze the following memory situations in terms of the parameters listed above, then use that information to decide on an appropriate strategy.

1. You go out with your family to do your Christmas shopping, and realize that you have forgotten your list.

2. The library tells you that you have not returned a book, and you try to recall whether you did or not.

3. You want to make sure you remember your dentist appointment.

4. You're reading a book about memory and want to remember the main points.

You will notice that many of the parameters of a memory situation do not really apply to retrieval tasks. For a retrieval task, the main concerns are (a) what type of information is it (what memory domain is involved), and (b) relevant aspects of the retrieval context.

Think through a situation

A strategic thinker, as we have seen, doesn't stop thinking strategically once she has decided on her strategy. A strategic thinker monitors her learning, and if necessary, tries different strategies.

Take your personal style into account

Effective strategy use is more difficult for those who are habitually impulsive. Such people tend to stop too soon when collecting evidence and often fail to take critical information into account. Thoughtful consideration is required to be a successful strategist. Nor does it help if you are habitually anxious. Strategy planning requires quite a lot of working memory—anxious people reduce their working memory capacity by using some of it for emotional information (thinking negatively about themselves, for example).

This should certainly not be taken to mean that you cannot become a strategic thinker if you are naturally impulsive or anxious. Rather, it should be taken as a warning that

```
┌─────────────────────────┐
│      Specify goal       │
└─────────────────────────┘
            ⇓
┌─────────────────────────┐
│      Analyse task       │
└─────────────────────────┘
            ⇓
┌─────────────────────────┐
│    Decide encoding      │
│       strategy          │
└─────────────────────────┘
            ⇓
┌─────────────────────────┐
│    Monitor learning     │
└─────────────────────────┘
            ⇓
┌─────────────────────────┐
│    Switch strategies    │
│      (If necessary)     │
└─────────────────────────┘
```

personal characteristics need to be taken into account. If you tend to rush into things, you may have to work a little harder to inculcate strategic habits. If you are anxious, or tend to clutter up your mental working space with negative or distracting thoughts, you need to spend some time and effort on strategies that help improve the quality of your attention.

But, while personal style affects your learning, the most important factors in whether or not you adopt and persist with good memory strategies are:

- Your knowledge of how memory works.
- Your faith in yourself and the strategies.

Putting it together

A strategic thinker:

- Knows a number of memory strategies.

- Has practiced them sufficiently so that their appropriate use is habitual and automatic.

- Has a broad knowledge of those situations when it is appropriate to use these strategies.

- Can intentionally extend the use of well-known strategies to new memory situations.

- Switches tactics as required.

- Knows that how well they remember depends on making an effort to use appropriate strategies.

- Knows that the time spent on strategy planning is time well-spent.

- Has a wide knowledge base.

Answers to exercises:

1. Retrieval task. Involves memory for other people and memory for personal events (your decisions as to who gets what). You're in a group situation (and the others in the group may help you in recalling items). There will be cues in the shops. But you're probably feeling frazzled, and there is probably some urgency in getting it all done on that occasion.

You're probably best to make a new list—the act of writing down will help recall the previous action of making a list, as well as relieve the load on working memory, and reduce your stress. Start by writing down all the people you have to get presents for, then try and attach present suggestions. Category labels (Chemist's shop; books; clothes, etc) will help.

2. Retrieval task. Involves memory for specific events. You're in the right environment for retrieving the information (assuming you're at the library), and so there are plenty of cues around. However, the familiarity of the environment also works against you—you need to search for something *distinctive* about your last visit.

    You do this by searching for cues, for example:

    ⇒ Can you clearly remember the last time you visited the library? No.

    ⇒ When do you usually go? Before tennis, therefore Monday evening.

    ⇒ Did you go last week? Yes.

    ⇒ Can you remember the visit now? No.

    ⇒ Look at the books you took out on that occasion.

    ⇒ Can you remember getting them out? Yes.

    ⇒ Now can you remember the visit? Yes.

    ⇒ Do you remember returning your books? No.

    ⇒ Can you remember any other books you returned? Yes.

    ⇒ Try to visualize these books.

    ⇒ Now can you remember the missing book? Yes!

3. Encoding task. Involves planning memory. The information is meaningless. It is presented on an appointment card. You need to remember the information until you have had the appointment. You don't need to remember all the information at one time—you could focus on the day, until the day arrives, and then focus on the time. There may be environmental constraints on the way in which you can encode this information externally (that is, your use of diaries, calendars, etc).

Your best strategy probably involves the use of an appropriate external aid (including asking someone to remind you). An appropriate internal strategy would involve linking the appointment with some useful trigger event.

4. Encoding task. Involves knowledge memory. The information is meaningful. It is presented in a written document that is complex, but not difficult. You want to remember the information in order to (a) develop expertise in human memory, and/or (b) use it to improve your remembering skills. You want to remember the information forever. You only need to remember the meaning, not the exact words. You can probably schedule your encoding for a time and place that is favorable for attention.

The appropriate strategy (set of strategies, really, because a number would need to be involved in a task as complex as this) involves building understanding through multiple connections. You need to choose study strategies that encourage you to search for the underlying relationships, integrate separate sections of text, etc.

———

Chapter 13

Putting It Into Practice

Whether you improve your memory is not determined by how intelligent you are, how educated you are, or how old you are. It is determined by your understanding and your mastery of effective memory strategies. Mastery is achieved through practice in different situations. Understanding is achieved by grasping the fundamental principles of how memory works and seeing how they apply to those strategies.

If you have read this book diligently you should now understand the basic principles of how memory works, and—most importantly—see how they underlie effective memory strategies.

If you understand *why* specific strategies are effective, you will know *when* they will be effective. And you will have confidence in them.

But it is not enough to be convinced of a strategy's effectiveness.

The cost of memory strategies

Cost (in time and effort) is a major reason that strategies of known effectiveness are so little used. Cost is determined not only by the demands of the strategy itself, but also by how well you have practiced the strategy. The less well you learn a strategy, the more time and effort it will take to apply it. On the other hand, even a basically costly strategy (one that takes considerable time to master) will become much less demanding if sufficiently well practiced. People's use of external memory aids is an example of the principle that cost is often more important than effectiveness.

These are the most frequently used memory strategies:

⇒ Writing calendar or diary notes.

⇒ Putting things in a special place.

⇒ Writing reminder notes.

⇒ Writing shopping lists.

⇒ Using face-name associations.

⇒ Mentally rehearsing information.

⇒ Using a timer.

⇒ Asking someone else to help.

All but two of these are external memory aids. Why? Not because they're so effective. Because they are easy to use.

What are the preferred internal strategies? Mentally retracing (a retrieval strategy) and mentally rehearsing (an encoding strategy). Not the most effective strategies—but the least costly. Asking someone to help you remember is also a popular strategy—somewhat to the surprise of researchers—but its popularity is readily understandable. It may not be particularly effective, but it is the least costly strategy of all!

Older people in particular are less inclined to use a strategy merely because it is effective. For them it is much more important that a strategy be familiar and easy to use (i.e., not cost much).

**If you want to use
effective strategies,
you must practice them.**

How to achieve permanent memory improvement

•❖ **Decide** what tasks you are interested in improving.

•❖ **Look** at the strategies appropriate for that particular task.

•❖ **Choose** which strategies suit *you*.

•❖ **Practice** those strategies on varying tasks until you can do them without thinking.

•❖ **Master** one task before going on to the next.

This book is not primarily a describer of memory strategies—although a number of strategies have had to be discussed. There are many books which describe specific strategies. The role of this book is to teach you to be a *user* of strategies.

The key to being a successful user is to be a strategic thinker, and for that, you must develop an *awareness* of memory. Get into the habit (develop the skill) of asking yourself: Is this worth remembering? When you're reading the paper—"Do I want to remember this?" When your partner tells you something—"Do I need to remember this?" When you meet a new person—"Do I want to remember this person?"

This sounds rather cold-blooded, but the developing of this awareness is critical to improving your memory. You need to *attend* to encode effectively.

Smart selection is better than total recall.

Our world today is increasingly complex and busy. The demands on memory are far greater than they have ever been. And we all feel inadequate in the face of these demands.

Don't feel inadequate. Forgetting is not a sign of stupidity. Nor is it a sign of growing old. Forgetting is sensible.

Don't aim to remember everything. Focus on remembering what is important.

And when you do forget something that is important, don't say "My mind's going," "I'm hopeless," "I can't remember anything." Say, "I should have encoded that information better," and learn from your mistake.

Putting it all together

To create effective memory codes

Select the important bits   **Attend** to the information   **Connect** them to accessible codes

Understand the information

To **select** effectively

The general principle is to select distinctive information— what is distinctive depends on the domain

Many study strategies help select information in knowledge memory

To **connect** effectively

The general principle is to seek the underlying relationship between information

Mnemonic strategies (elaborative transformation) can connect information that is not meaningful

To **attend** effectively

There are strategies to improve the quality of your attention

There are strategies to direct your attention appropriately

TESTS OF WORKING MEMORY CAPACITY

These tests are included for your interest, to give you an idea of your working memory span. Because they are not being administered in controlled conditions, you should not regard them as definitive.

Digit span

This test of your working memory capacity for digits requires the involvement of another person. The tester reads out each sequence of digits, one sequence at a time, at a rate of one digit per second. The person being tested then repeats the sequence back. Some sequences have five digits, some six, and so on up to eight. There are six sequences of each number of digits. The second three of each series should be repeated back in *reverse* order.

Series of five digits:

47912

83524

62471

to be repeated back in reverse order:

90257

16385

54036

Series of six digits:

2 9 8 4 3 1

7 1 6 9 0 8

3 8 1 6 9 0

to be repeated back in reverse order:

0 5 7 1 8 3

9 2 0 3 4 7

4 7 2 0 5 9

Series of seven digits:

1 6 4 8 2 5 3

5 0 3 7 1 2 6

8 3 7 5 6 4 0

to be repeated back in reverse order:

6 4 5 2 7 1 9

4 1 8 3 5 7 2

3 9 0 4 8 6 1

Series of eight digits:

2 5 9 0 3 8 4 7

0 7 1 6 9 3 5 4

9 2 6 1 0 5 8 3

to be repeated back in reverse order:

7 8 2 9 4 0 3 6

1 4 0 5 7 2 9 8

5 9 3 4 1 6 7 2

An average adult can repeat correctly 2/3 sequences of seven digits. An above average adult can repeat correctly a sequence of eight digits, and say in reverse order a sequence of seven or more.

Word span

The tester reads out the following words, one set at a time, at a rate of one word per second. The person being tested then repeats the sequence back. Initially the sets have two words. The number of words in a set increases steadily to seven. Stop when you reach the point at which you are unable to recall all words in the correct order, for all three sets of the same size. The level at which you were correct for two of the three sets is the measure of your word span.

stairs	meat					
wheel	hour					
tea	fire					
bread	lawn	shoe				
house	book	egg				
moth	cheese	spoon				
time	plate	milk	deer			
floor	port	thing	map			
soup	wall	heart	dog			
duck	cash	hand	roof	train		
bed	knife	day	nose	shirt		
ear	bus	jam	man	shelf		
cake	door	fog	mouse	skirt	week	
wife	pea	socks	month	goose	car	
bath	cup	horse	oil	son	work	
bank	dress	fruit	love	room	year	wasp
wine	suit	pig	lamp	hair	beach	clock
bean	cow	light	hat	thief	day	pain

Spans for American college students in this exercise ranged from 4 to 6.

Reading span

The following sentences are to be read aloud, one sentence at a time (cover the text above and below so that you can't see the sentences you have read or the ones you are about to read). At the end of a set, you need to try and recall the last word of each sentence.

The car turned into the drive and they saw the house for the first time.

She came across the room and bent to pick up the dress discarded on the floor.

The pig grunted noisily, then heaved itself to its feet and came across to the wall.

He wondered when the van would get here so that he could start work.

In the morning no tracks could be seen in the heavy dew that blanketed the grass.

Long ago there were kauris here, and now there is only the road.

She was lost in the sky and the balloon was coming down at a frightening speed.

The fog was thick and the crane was a spectral shadow in the ominous silence.

The wine was pleasant but she wondered what would happen when it had been drunk.

Down among the reeds edging the lake he found the limp body of his dog.

On a clear day you could see right across the valley to the swamp.

The boy noticed that the duck seemed to have no fear of people.

He washed up on the beach two days after the worst storm in living memory.

The apples were particularly crisp and went very nicely with the spicy cheese.

The words ran into each other and the room began to spin around him.

The violinist bowed to the audience who applauded madly and stamped their feet.

For many months the crayfish walk right around the islands along the seabed.

He advanced upon the trembling animal, the knife gleaming in his massive hand.

When we heard the bells ring, our first thought was relief that it had finally happened.

She climbed to the top, then stood poised on the very edge of the cliff.

Lost in his memories he stepped out blindly right into the path of the truck.

The little girl asked the teacher whether she could go out and play.

The paper was very gloomy about the possibility of prices rising to an all-time high.

The room was tidy and the bed was made but crayon marked the walls.

He set the table carefully and stepped back to admire the effect of the silver candles.

On the day the wall collapsed I was busy tidying the garden for the party.

The bus stopped with a screech and the old man furiously waved his stick.

The water was calm as a millpond and the sails hung limply on the yachts.

She picked up the phone and paused to consider the stain on the carpet.

The shop was packed with hysterical customers on the first day of the annual sale.

The light plane seemed to hang in the air for a heart-stopping moment.

In the evening the mosquitoes came out and whined tirelessly around the fire.

The supermarket trolley spun out of her hands and careered into the old lady.

The boss came in late and snapped at the offer of a cup of coffee.

Oranges and lemons were piled in pyramids on the stalls and glowed in the sun.

When the train arrived five minutes early the waiting passengers all checked the clock.

The chocolate poured out, thick and luscious, over the mound of soft berries.

In the days before cars far more people knew how to ride a horse.

Listening at the keyhole he heard the soft tap of her heels cross the floor.

The river was rising fast but soon they would have all the furniture in the attic.

As the thief ran desperately along the narrow plank, he dropped the jar.

For the last time the ship sailed into the harbor and waited for the small boats.

Among American college students (presumably "above average" in terms of reading comprehension), reading spans range from 2 to 5.5. High span is defined as 4 and above; medium span as 3-3.5; low as below 3.

GLOSSARY

accessible: a memory code is accessible when it is readily activated.

acoustic: the sound of a word.

acronym: uses the initial letters of a list of items to form a meaningful word (e.g., FACE for the notes in the spaces of the treble staff)

acrostic: uses the initial letters of a list of items as the initial letters of other words to make a meaningful phrase (e.g., *Every Good Boy Deserves Fruit* for the notes on the lines of the treble staff).

activate: make a memory code active—to raise its energy level so that it becomes available to you.

active reading: strategies that promote the effective selection of important information by encouraging active involvement in the reading process.

active: the state in which a memory code can be looked at and worked with.

alphabet search: a generation strategy which uses the letters of the alphabet as recall cues.

associative stage: the second stage in the process of learning a skill, in which action steps become coordinated and their sequence learned.

autobiographical memory: a component of personal memory. The memory domain that holds information about yourself, and in particular, about the events and experiences that have happened to you.

autonomous stage: the final stage in the process of learning a skill, in which the action sequence has become so well-learned that it no longer requires verbal reminders.

biographical codes: another term for semantic codes, to more clearly distinguish semantic codes from visually-derived semantic codes.

bit: the smallest amount of information possible. A memory code is made up of a number of bits.

causal chain: the bones of a story: a string of causal connections from the protagonist's goal to the outcome.

chunk: a tight cluster of information identified by a pronounceable label and able to be treated as a single unit when worked with.

clustering: connecting memory codes with many, strong links, to the extent that activation of any one code will automatically activate all codes in the cluster.

code: information that has been manipulated and transformed by discarding some bits, and emphasizing others.

context effect: the ease with which you can remember something is a function of the degree to which the context in which you are trying to retrieve the information matches the context in which you originally encoded it.

context: the information contained in the situation in which you are encoding or retrieving the target information. It includes the physical environment and your own physical, mental, and emotional state, as well as information presented at the same time as the target.

deep approach: an approach to learning that emphasizes the underlying principles and relationships between details.

digit span: the number of digits that you can correctly repeat back, in the correct order. A measure of working memory capacity.

distinctiveness principle: memory codes are easier to find when they can be easily distinguished from other, related codes.

domino principle: the principle that activating one memory code will cause other, linked, codes to be activated also.

elaborative interrogation: a non-transformational strategy involving turning the facts to be learned into why-questions.

emotional memory: a component of autobiographical memory. The memory domain that holds your memory of how you felt on particular occasions.

encoding: transforming information into a memory code, and placing it in your memory.

environmental aid: a physical object or event that cues memory.

event memory: includes memory for specific events that have happened to you, as well as general event *scripts*, and a potted summary.

face-name association: is a variant of the keyword method for remembering people's names.

fan effect: because there is only so much activation to go around, the more memory codes that are activated, the less activation each one receives. Retrieval becomes slower and more difficult.

first-letter mnemonic: a list-learning strategy that uses the initial letters of the items to aid recall. There are two types: acronyms and acrostics.

forgetting: not being able to find a memory code.

frequency effect: a memory code is easier to access the more often it has been activated in the past.

generation strategy: a search strategy that enables you to systematically produce a number of possible recall cues.

goal: your articulation of the target at the beginning of your search. The more specific it is, the more likely your search will be successful, and the more likely you are to recognize that you have indeed reached your target.

graphic organizers: a type of graphic summary appropriate for material that can be expressed hierarchically, that allows the comparison of between-cluster relations.

graphic summaries: summarize the main points of a text in a different format than the straightforward string of statements.

headings: single words or phrases that label sections in a text and help organize it in a hierarchical structure.

highlighting: any way of emphasizing key words or phrases, such as underlining, framing, using bold type, or using a colored marker.

identity memory: includes separate domains for physical features; facial expression; semantic information (e.g., occupation, marital status, address, etc); visual information (e.g., gender, approximate age, ethnicity, etc); and names. A component of social memory.

imagery: the use of visual images to encode non-visual information.

internal representation: a neural event in the brain that holds your version of some information event.

keyword method: transforms a word into an image via a keyword—a word derived from the word to be learned, that is imageable. The keyword method is useful for linking pairs of items—a word with its meaning, a capital with its country, a country with its product.

knowledge memory: the memory domain concerned with general, encyclopedic knowledge of the world, and language. Also known as semantic memory, or sometimes, reference memory.

learning style: your predisposition to apply particular encoding strategies.

link method: has no well-learned anchors, but simply links items in a chain of paired items.

list-learning strategies: include three strategies using imagery to link items in a list: the place method, the pegword method, and the link method; and two strategies using words to link items: the story method, and first-letter mnemonics.

maintenance rehearsal: simple repetition to hold an item in working memory.

maps: graphic summaries that display main ideas in a structured but non-hierarchical format.

matching effect: the more closely the code and retrieval cue match, the easier a memory code is to find.

memory domain: a part of memory that deals with information of a specific type, and has its own principles of organization.

mind-mapping: a mapping strategy made famous in a number of books by Tony Buzan.

mnemonic strategies: are aids to memory such as acronyms, acrostics, techniques that link information by creating visual images or making up a story. They are most suitable for information that is not inherently meaningful.

monitoring: strategies to inform you how well you have learned the information in a memory situation so that you can plan your encoding strategies appropriately.

multimedia summaries: graphic summaries that combine pictures and text in an integrated manner. Especially appropriate for demonstrating scientific explanations.

name code: the memory code that contains the person's name. It is only accessible through the semantic codes.

network: the structure of memory—memory codes that are connected to each other.

non-transformational elaboration: elaborating information to make it more memorable by linking it with familiar information that is meaningfully connected.

outcome goals: your objective in carrying out a learning task, in terms of the desired outcome.

outlines: a type of graphic summary appropriate for material that can be expressed hierarchically.

pegword method: similar to the place method, but uses numbers as pegs or anchors. Images for the numbers are rote-learned by means of a rhyme. The pegword method can be extended using a coding system.

personal memory: the memory domain that holds information about people—yourself and others. Includes information about events and experiences, feelings and beliefs, behavior and identity. Sometimes called episodic memory.

place method: traditionally known as the method of loci. Images of items to be remembered are visualized at familiar landmarks, in a set order.

planning memory: memory for intentions that we wish to carry out in the future. Sometimes called prospective memory.

priming effect: a memory code is more ready to activate, and so easier to access, when memory codes linked to it have been recently activated.

process goals: specific intermediate objectives that need to be achieved on the way to producing the desired outcome of a learning task.

reading span: a measure of working memory capacity that is related to your ability to understand written and spoken information.

recency effect: a memory code is more readily activated when it has recently been activated.

relational images: visual images that bring together at least two items.

repetition: repeating information is the simplest learning strategy, and is effective because of the *frequency effect.*

re-statement: paraphrasing information in your own words.

retrieval or *recall cues:* information that prompts your memory search.

retrieving: finding a memory code—transforming it from a database memory code into an active working memory code.

script: a generalized outline or composite framework that has been constructed from a number of specific examples.

secondary recall cues: the memory codes whose connections define the trail of your memory search.

self-description: a component of autobiographical memory. The memory domain that holds the information that makes up your "self"—your identity information.

semantic codes: memory codes that contain information about the person—their occupation, whether they have a partner, children, etc.

semantic: the meaning of a word.

skill memory: the memory domain that deals with motor skills, such as playing a musical instrument; and cognitive skills, such as reading or computer programming.

skimming: skipping speedily through text actively searching for critical information.

social memory: contains your memory for other people—their identity (which itself breaks down into three different types of information), biographical details, and memory for their behavior. A component of personal memory.

spacing effect: repetition is far more effective when it occurs at spaced intervals, rather than at one time.

structural codes: memory codes that contain information about physical features of a person.

study strategies: encoding strategies that help you understand and recall meaningful information, in particular factual information from books or oral presentations.

super cluster effect: if memory codes are sufficiently well integrated, clusters can be activated as a single unit. Accordingly, even when many memory codes are activated, if they are strongly clustered, retrieval is not hindered.

super cluster: clusters of codes can be linked to other clusters. To the extent that the connections are strong, the network of clusters can be treated as one super cluster.

support strategies: strategies that support your encoding and retrieval skills.

surface approach: an approach to learning that emphasizes superficial similarities between details, and is concerned with reproducing information rather than understanding it.

taking notes: strategies that promote the effective selection of important information by re-stating and re-organizing textual material.

target: the memory code you wish to retrieve.

theme: a single word or phrase that unites the bits of information in a cluster.

topical summaries: summarize the main points of a text point by point.

transformational elaboration: elaborating information to make it more memorable by transforming it into an interactive image.

transformational elaborative strategies: strategies that link new information with familiar memory codes through transformation. They include the keyword method and face-name association, which use imagery; and the coding method, which transforms numbers into words.

trigger events: events that trigger intended activities.

visually-derived semantic codes: memory codes that contain that information about a person that can be discerned simply be looking at them—for example, their approximate height, their gender, etc.

word span: the number of words you can repeat back in the correct order. A measure of working memory capacity that affects your ability to acquire new and foreign vocabulary.

working memory: that state of memory in which memory codes can be looked at and worked with.

working memory capacity: the amount of information you can hold and work with at one time.

RECOMMENDED READING

Specific strategies

Mnemonic strategies

There are a number of books available that describe mnemonic strategies, for example:

Buzan, Tony *Use Your Memory*. London: BBC, 1974 (reprinted 1984;1986;1989).

Since a major value of mnemonic strategies is to acquire foreign languages, it is worth noting that Dr Michael Gruneberg (an academic who has focused on practical applications of memory research) has written several books using the "Linkword" system (a keyword strategy) to learn German, Italian, Spanish, and French, for example:

Gruneberg, Michael M. *German by association*. Passport Books, 1994.

Mind Maps

Tony Buzan has written a number of books on mind-mapping, his own version of a mapping strategy. The latest one is called *The Mind Map Book* (BBC, 1993), which is very visual (lots of pictures, illustrations etc). If you prefer something more strictly factual, you might prefer his very popular early book: *Use Your Head* (BBC, 1974; reprinted 1982; 1984; 1985; 1986; 1987; 1989).

Study skills

There are a number of books available that discuss study strategies, such as:

Winder, John *Learning Success: A Practical Guide for Learners Who Want Results*. Auckland: ESA Publications Ltd., 1994.

For a more academic approach, there is:

Baine, David *Memory and Instruction*. Englewood Cliffs, NJ: Educational Technology Publications, 1986.

Biggs, J.B. and Moore, P.J. *The Process of Learning* (3rd ed.) Sydney: Prentice-Hall, 1993.

This book also discusses learning styles.

Learning styles

Harrison, A.F. and Bramson, R.M. *The Art of Thinking*. New York, Anchor Press, 1982.

Although this is not strictly about the type of learning styles I have been talking about, this is an interesting and readable book about different styles of thinking. For a more academic discussion about the specific learning styles I have discussed, you could read:

Ramsden, Paul (ed.) *Improving learning: New Perspectives*. New York: Nichols Publishing Co. 1988.

General

Baddeley, Alan. *Your Memory: A User's Guide*. (New edition). London: Penguin Books, 1994.

Gruneberg, Michael M. and Herrmann, Douglas J. *Your Memory For Life!* London: Blandford, 1997.

Higbee, Kenneth L. *Your Memory: How It Works and How to Improve it*. (2nd ed.) Prentice Hall Press, 1988.

These four authors are all academics in the field of memory research and know what they're talking about. The first two books in particular are very readable.

References

Anderson, J.R. *Cognitive psychology and Its Implications*. San Francisco: W.H. Freeman and Co., 1980.

Anderson, J.R., J.M. Fincham, and S. Douglass. "The Role of Examples and Rules in the Acquisition of a Cognitive Skill." *Journal of Experimental Psychology: Learning, Memory and Cognition* 23 (1997): 932-945.

Baddeley, A. *Your Memory: A User's Guide*. London: Penguin Books, 1994.

Baine, D. *Memory and Instruction*. Englewood Cliffs, NJ: Educational Technology Publications, 1986.

Barnett, J.E., F.J. DiVesta, and J.T. Rogozinski. "What is Learned in Note-Taking." *Journal of Educational Psychology* 73 (1981): 181-192.

Barsalou, L.W. "The Content and Organization of Autobiographical Memories." In *Remembering Reconsidered: Ecological and Traditional Approaches to the Study of Memory*, edited by U. Neisser and E. Winograd. Cambridge: Cambridge University Press, 1988.

Begg, I. "Imagery and Organization in Memory: Instructional Effects." *Memory and Cognition* 6 (1978):173-174.

Belleza, F.S. "Mnemonic-device instruction with adults." In *Cognitive Strategy Research: Psychological Foundations*, edited by M. Pressley and J.R. Levin. New York: Springer-Verlag, 1983.

Best, J.B.. *Cognitive Psychology*. 3rd ed. St. Paul, Minn.: West Publishing, 1992.

Bevan, W. and Steger, J.A. "Free Recall and Abstractness of Stimuli." *Science* 172 (1971): 597-599.

Biggs, J.B., and P.J. Moore, *The Process of Learning*. 3rd ed. Sydney: Prentice-Hall, 1993.

Bower, G.H. "Mental Imagery and Associative Learning." In *Cognition in Learning and Memory*, edited by L.W. Gregg. New York: Wiley, 1972.

Bower, G.H., and M.C. Clark. "Narrative Stories as Mediators for Serial Learning." *Psychonomic Science* 14 (1969): 181-182.

Bower, G.H., M.C. Clark, A.M. Lesgold, and D. Winzenz, "Hierarchical Retrieval Schemes in Recall of Categorized Word Lists." *Journal of Verbal Learning and Verbal Behavior* 8 (1969): 323-343.

Bransford, J.D., B.S. Stein, T.S. Shelton, and R.A. Owings. "Cognition and Adaptation: The Importance of Learning to Learn." In *Cognition, Social Behavior and the Environment*, edited by J. Harvey. Hillsdale, NJ: Erlbaum, 1981.

Bransford, J.D., B.S. Stein, N.J. Vye, J.J. Franks, P.M. Auble, K.J. Mezynski, and G.A. Perfetto. "Differences in Approaches to Learning: An Overview." *Journal of Experimental Psychology: General* 111 (1982): 390-398.

Bretzing, B.H., and R.W. Kulhavy. "Note-taking and Passage Style." *Journal of Educational Psychology* 73 (1981): 242-250.

Broadbent, D.E., P.J. Cooper, and M.H. Broadbent. "A Comparison of Hierarchical and Matrix Retrieval Schemes in Recall." *Journal of Experimental Psychology: Human Learning and Memory* 4 (1978): 486-497.

Bruce, V. and T. Valentine. "Identity priming in the recognition of familiar faces." *British Journal of Psychology* 76 (1985): 373-383.

Bruce, V., and A. Young. "Understanding face recognition." *British Journal of Psychology* 77 (1986): 1-23.

Bruce, V. "Changing Faces: Visual and Non-Visual Coding Processes in Face Recognition." *British Journal of Psychology* 73 (1982): 105-116.

Cantor, J., and R. W. Engle. "Working-Memory Capacity as Long-Term Memory Activation: An Individual-Differences Approach." *Journal of Experimental Psychology: Learning, Memory and Cognition* 19 (1993): 1101-1114.

Caspari, I., S.R. Parkinson, L.L. LaPointe, and R.C. Katz. "Working Memory and Aphasia." *Brain and Cognition* 37 (1998): 205-223.

Chase, W.G., and K.A. Ericsson. "Skilled Memory." In *Cognitive Skills and Their Acquisition*, edited by J.R. Anderson. Hillsdale, NJ: Erlbaum, 1981.

Daneman, M. and P. A. Carpenter. "Individual Differences in Working Memory and Reading." *Journal of Verbal Learning and Verbal Behavior* 19 (1980): 450-466.

Eizenberg, N. "Approaches to Learning Anatomy: Developing a Program for Preclinical Medical Students." In *Improving Learning: New Perspectives*, edited by P. Ramsden. New York: Nichols Publishing, 1988.

Engle, R.W., J. Cantor, and J.J. Carullo. "Individual Differences in Working Memory and Comprehension: A Test of Four Hypotheses." *Journal of Experimental Psychology: Learning, Memory and Cognition* 18 (1992): 972-992.

Entwhistle, N., and P. Ramsden. *Understanding Student Learning.* Kent, England: Croom Helm, 1983.

Folkard, S., and T.H. Monk. "Time of Day Effects In Immediate and Delayed Memory." In *Practical Aspects of Memory*, edited by M.M. Gruneberg, P.E. Morris, and R.N. Sykes. London: Academic Press, 1978.

Gathercole, S.E., C.S. Willis, A.D. Baddeley, and H. Emslie. "The Children's Test of Nonword Repetition: A Test of Phonological Working Memory." *Memory* 2 (1994): 103-127.

Glanzer, M., L. Koppenaal, and R. Nelson. "Effects of Relations Between Words on Short-Term Storage and Long-Term Storage." *Journal of Verbal Learning and Verbal Behavior* 11 (1972): 403-416.

Glass, A.L., K.J. Holyoak, and J.L. Santa. *Cognition*. Reading, Mass.: Addison-Wesley, 1979.

Gruneberg, M.M. "The Practical Applications of Memory Aids: Knowing How, Knowing When, and Knowing When Not." In *Aspects of Memory*. Vol. 1, *The Practical Aspects*. 2nd ed., edited by M.M. Gruneberg and P. Morris. London: Routledge, 1992.

Gruneberg, M. M., and D. J. Herrmann. *Your memory for life!* London: Blandford, 1997.

Herrmann, D.J. "Task Appropriateness of Mnemonic Techniques." *Perceptual and Motor Skills* 64 (1987): 171-178.

Herrmann, D.J., and M. Palmisiano. "The Facilitation of Memory Performance." In *Aspects of Memory*. Vol. 1, *The Practical Aspects*. 2nd ed., edited by M.M. Gruneberg and P. Morris. London: Routledge, 1992.

Herrmann, D.J., and A. Searleman. "The New Multimodal Approach to Memory Improvement." In *Advances in Learning and Motivation*, edited by G. Bower. New York: Academic Press, 1990.

Herz, R.S. "The Effects of Cue Distinctiveness on Odor-Based Context-Dependent Memories." *Memory and Cognition* 25 (1997): 375-380.

Higbee, K.L. "Some Pseudo-Limitations of Mnemonics." In *Practical Aspects of Memory*, edited by M.M. Gruneberg, P.E. Morris, and R.N. Sykes. London: Academic Press, 1978.

Hunt, R. R., and J. M. Elliott. "The Role of Nonsemantic Information in Memory: Orthographic Distinctiveness Effects on Retention." *Journal of Experimental Psychology: General* 109 (1980): 49-74.

Intons-Peterson, M.J., and J. Fourrier. "External and Internal Memory Aids: When and How Often Do We Use Them?" *Journal of Experimental Psychology: General* 115 (1986): 267-280.

Intons-Peterson, M.J. and G.L. Newsome III. "External Memory Aids: Effects and Effectiveness." In *Memory Improvement: Implications for Memory Theory*, edited by D. Herrmann, H. Weingartner, A. Searleman, and C. McEvoy. New York: Springer-Verlag, 1992.

Jones, B.F. "Text Learning Strategy Instruction: Guidelines From Theory and Practice. In *Learning and Study Strategies*, edited by C.E. Weinstein, E.T. Goetz, and P.A. Alexander. New York: Academic Press, 1986.

Jones, D.M., D.R. Davies, K.M. Hogan, J. Patrick, and W.G. Cumberbatch. "Short-Term Memory During the Normal Working Day." In *Practical Aspects of Memory*, edited by M.M. Gruneberg, P.E. Morris and R.N. Sykes. London: Academic Press, 1978.

Just, M.A., and P.A. Carpenter. "A Capacity Theory of Comprehension: Individual Differences in Working Memory." *Psychological Review* 99 (1992): 122-149.

King, J., and M.A. Just. "Individual Differences in Syntactic Processing: The Role of Working Memory." *Journal of Memory and Language* 30 (1991): 580-602.

Light, L.L., F. Kayra-Stuart, and S. Hollander. "Recognition Memory for Typical and Unusual Faces." *Journal of Experimental Psychology: Human Learning and Memory* 5 (1979): 212-228.

Lorch, R.F. Jr., and E.P. Lorch. "Effects of Organizational Signals on Text-Processing Strategies." *Journal of Educational Psychology* 87 (1995): 537-544.

Lorch, R.F. Jr., and E.P. Lorch. "Effects of Organizational Signals on Free Recall of Expository Text. *Journal of Educational Psychology 88* (1996): 38-48.

Mandler, G. 1967. Organization and memory. In K.W. Spence and J.T. Spence (eds.) *The psychology of learning and motivation. Vol.1.* New York: Academic Press.

Mandler, G. and Z. Pearlstone. "Free and Constrained Concept Learning and Subsequent Recall." *Journal of Verbal Learning and Verbal Behavior* 5 (1966):126-131.

Marks, D.F. "Individual Differences in the Vividness of Visual Imagery and Their Effect on Function." In *The Function and Nature of Imagery*, edited by P.W. Sheehan. New York: Academic Press, 1972.

Mayer, R.E., W. Bove, A. Bryman, R. Mars, and L. Tapangco. "When Less is More: Meaningful Learning From Visual and Verbal Summaries of Science Textbook Lessons." *Journal of Educational Psychology* 88 (1996): 64-73.

McCarty, D.L. "Investigation of a Visual Imagery Mnemonic Device for Acquiring Face-Name Associations." *Journal of Experimental Psychology: Human Learning and Memory* 6 (1980): 145-155.

McDaniel, M.A., and C.M. Donnelly. "Learning with Analogy and Elaborative Interrogation." *Journal of Educational Psychology* 8 (1996): 508-519.

Morris, P.E. "Sense and Nonsense in Traditional Mnemonics." In *Practical Aspects of Memory*, edited by M.M. Gruneberg, P.E. Morris, and R.N. Sykes. London: Academic Press, 1978.

Morris, P.E. "Strategies for Learning and Recall." In *Applied Problems in Memory*, edited by M.M. Gruneberg and P. Morris. London: Academic Press, 1979.

Morris, P.E. "Prospective Memory: Remembering To Do Things." In *Aspects of Memory*. Vol.1, *The Practical Aspects*. 2nd ed., edited by M.M. Gruneberg, and P. Morris. London: Routledge, 1992.

Murphy, G.L., and D.L. Medin. "The Role of Theories in Conceptual Coherence." *Psychological Review* 92 (1985): 289-316.

Myers, J.L., E.J. O'Brien, D.A. Balota, and M.L. Toyofuku. "Memory Search Without Interference: The Role of Integration." *Cognitive Psychology* 16 (1984): 217-242.

Nisbet, J., and J. Shucksmith. *Learning Strategies*. London: Routledge and Kegan Paul, 1986.

Paivio, A., M. Walsh, and T. Bons. "Concreteness Effects on Memory: When and Why?" *Journal of Experimental Psychology: Learning, Memory and Cognition* 20 (1994): 1196-1204.

Paivio, A., J.C. Yuille, and S.A. Madigan. "Concreteness, Imagery, and Meaningfulness Values for 925 Nouns." *Journal of Experimental Psychology Monograph Supplement* 76 (1968): 1-9.

Peper, R.J., and R.E. Mayer. "Note-Taking as a Generative Activity." *Journal of Educational Psychology* 70 (1978): 514-522.

Plude, D.J. "Attention and Memory Improvement." In *Memory Improvement: Implications for Memory Theory*, edited by D. Herrmann, H. Weingartner, A. Searleman, and C. McEvoy. New York: Springer-Verlag, 1992.

Pressley, M., and P.B. El-Dinary. "Memory Strategy Instruction That Promotes Good Information Processing." In *Memory Improvement: Implications for Memory Theory*, edited by D. Herrmann, H. Weingartner, A. Searleman, and C. McEvoy. New York: Springer-Verlag, 1992.

Pressley, M., J.R. Levin, J.W. Hall, G.E. Miller, and J.K. Berry. "The Keyword Method and Foreign Word Acquisition." *Journal of Experimental Psychology: Human Learning and Memory* 6 (1980): 163-173.

Rabinowitz, J.C., G. Mandler, and K.E. Patterson. "Determinants of Recognition and Recall: Accessibility and Generation." *Journal of Experimental Psychology: General* 106 (1977): 302-329.

Radvansky, G.A., and R.T. Zacks. "Mental Models and the Fan Effect." *Journal of Experimental Psychology: Learning, Memory and Cognition* 17 (1991): 940-953.

Rawles, R.E. "The Past and Present of Mnemotechny." In *Practical Aspects of Memory*, edited by M.M. Gruneberg, P.E. Morris, and R.N. Sykes. London: Academic Press, 1978.

Reynolds, R.E. and Shirey, L.L. "The Role of Attention in Studying and Learning." In *Learning and Study Strategies*, edited by C.E. Weinstein, E.T. Goetz, and P.A. Alexander. New York: Academic Press. 1986

Robinson, D.H., and K.A. Kiewra. "Visual Argument: Graphic Organizers are Superior to Outlines in Improving Learning from Text." *Journal of Educational Psychology* 87 (1995): 455-467.

Robinson, J.A. Autobiographical memory. In *Aspects of Memory.* Vol.1, *The Practical Aspects.* 2nd ed., edited by M.M. Gruneberg and P. Morris. London: Routledge, 1992.

Schewel, R. "Semantic Mapping: a Study Skills Strategy." *Academic Therapy, Special Issue* 24 (1989): 439-447.

Schmeck, R.R., ed. *Learning Strategies and Learning Styles.* New York: Plenum Press, 1988.

Schneider, W., and M. Pressley. *Memory Development Between Two and Twenty.* New York: Springer-Verlag, 1989.

Schraw, G., M. E. Dunkle, L. D. Bendixen, and T.D. Roedel. "Does a General Monitoring Skill Exist?" *Journal of Educational Psychology* 87 (1995): 433-444.

Shiffrin, R. M., and R. M. Nosofsky. "Seven Plus or Minus 2: A Commentary on Capacity Limitations." *Psychological Review* 101 (1994): 357-361.

Singer, M., P. Andrusiak, P. Reisdorf, and N. L. Black. "Individual Differences in Bridging Inference Processes." *Memory and Cognition* 20 (1992): 539-548.

Talbot, M. "Antonio Vivaldi." In *The New Grove Italian Baroque Masters*, edited by S. Sadie. London: Macmillan, 1980.

Thomas, J.R. "Noise and Memory." In *Practical aspects of memory*, edited by M.M. Gruneberg, P.E. Morris, and R.N. Sykes. London: Academic Press, 1978.

Thompson, C.P., Cowan, T.M., and Frieman, J. *Memory Search by a Memorist.* Hillsdale, N.J.: Lawrence Erlbaum Associates, 1993.

Tilley, A., and D. Statham. "The Effect of Prior Sleep on Retrieval." *Acta Psychologica* 70 (1989): 199-203.

Walczyk, J.J., and R. W. Taylor. "How Do the Efficiencies of Reading Subcomponents Relate to Looking Back in Text." *Journal of Educational Psychology* 88 (1996): 537-545.

Walker-Smith, G. J. "The Effects of Delay and Exposure Duration in a Face Recognition Task." *Perception and Psychophysics* 24 (1978): 63-70.

Wang, A. Y., and M. H. Thomas. "Effect of Keywords on Long-Term Retention: Help or Hindrance?" *Journal of Educational Psychology* 87 (1995): 468-475.

Weinland, J.D. *How to Improve Your Memory*. New York: Harper and Row, 1986.

West, L. "Implications of Recent Research for Improving Secondary School Science Learning." In *Improving Learning: New Perspectives*, edited by Paul Ramsden. New York: Nichols Publishing Co., 1988.

Willoughby, T., S. Desmarais, E. Wood, S. Sims, and M. Kalra. "Mechanisms that Facilitate the Effectiveness of Elaboration Strategies." *Journal of Educational Psychology* 89 (1997): 682-685.

Winnick, W. A., and K. Kressel. "Tachistoscopic Recognition Thresholds, Paired-Associate Learning, and Immediate Recall as a Function of Abstractness-Concreteness and Word Frequency." *Journal of Experimental Psychology* 70 (1965): 163-168.

Winograd, E., and V. E. Church. "Role of Spatial Location in Learning Face-Name Associations." *Memory and Cognition* 16 (1988): 1-7.

Wulf, G., and R. A. Schmidt. "Variability of Practice and Implicit Motor Learning." *Journal of Experimental Psychology: Learning, Memory and Cognition* 23 (1997): 987-1006.

Young, A. W., K. H. McWeeny, A. W. Ellis, and D. C. Hay. "Naming and Categorizing Faces and Written Names." *The Quarterly Journal of Experimental Psychology* 38A (1986): 297-318.

Zimmerman, B.J., D. Greenberg, and C.E. Weinstein. "Self-Regulating Academic Study Time: A Strategy Approach." In *Self-Regulation of Learning and Performance: Issues and Educational Applications*, edited by D.H. Schunk and B.J. Zimmerman. Hillsdale, N.J.: Lawrence Erlbaum Associates, 1994.

Zimmerman, B.J., and A. Kitsantas. "Developmental Phases in Self-Regulation: Shifting From Process Goals to Outcome Goals." *Journal of Educational Psychology* 89 (1997): 29-36.

INDEX